Elementary Introduction to Number Theory

Under the general editorship of

DAVID VERNON WIDDER
Harvard University

Elementary

Introduction

to

NUMBER THEORY

CALVIN T. LONG
Washington State University

D. C. HEATH AND COMPANY
Lexington, Massachusetts

Preface

THIS BOOK is designed for a one-semester course in the theory of numbers at a level somewhat below that of the usual introductory college course. It is the result of the eight-year development of a course taught to undergraduate mathematics and mathematics-education majors at the sophomore-junior level and to participants in National Science Foundation Summer Institutes. Except in Chapter 3, no background is presumed other than the equivalent of a course in college algebra. In particular, knowledge of the calculus is not presumed except in two sections of Chapter 3, and those results depending on the calculus may be omitted by students lacking this background. The text should prove to be particularly appropriate for use in teacher pre-service and in-service training programs.

In attempting to make the material accessible to the intended audience, an effort has been made to give especially complete and detailed arguments, il-lustrating definitions, theorems, and subtleties of proof with explicit numerical examples whenever possible. An attempt has also been made to organize the results and construct the arguments in such a way as to reveal the essential structure of the subject and to impart an understanding of the various methods of proof as *methods* rather than *tricks*.

Since learning mathematics involves doing mathematics, some 300 exercises have been distributed throughout the text at the ends of the sections. These range in difficulty from simple numerical problems and direct applications of results in the text to extensions of the theory and to exercises which endeavor to lead the student to discover results for himself. Many of the exercises contain hints to aid the student in finding solutions. Answers to selected exercises, including many proofs, are given at the back of the book. In no case is the development of the theory made to depend on the result of an exercise.

Since this book is intentionally small, some of the topics usually treated in an introductory course have been omitted. Those discussed were chosen because they are basic to any study of the theory of numbers and because they have proved to be of special interest to the author and his students. The discussion of mathematical induction and well-ordering in Chapter 1, a topic not usually covered in such a course, is treated here in considerable detail since students at the sophomore-junior level frequently have only the most rudimentary knowledge of these important and useful ideas. Of necessity, the discussion of prime numbers in Chapter 3 is largely expository, but it was felt that the notions involved are so intrinsically interesting that they should be presented in as much detail as possible. The discussion of multiplicative number-theoretic functions in Chapter 6 leads to a particularly nice derivation of the formula for $\phi(n)$ and to some interesting generalizations.

In an effort to impart some sense of historical perspective, many of the theorems and proofs have been attributed to their discoverers, although no effort has been made to be complete in this detail. I am also indebted to many other writers, to colleagues, and to students, all of whom have had an influence on the development of this book. Particular thanks are due to Professor James H. Jordan, who carefully read the original manuscript and offered many helpful criticisms, and to the staff of D. C. Heath and Company for their help and consideration. Finally, I would like to acknowledge my debt of gratitude to Professor Ivan Niven, whose exciting and impeccable lectures first introduced me to this delightful study. It is my hope that some of that same sense of excitement has been captured in these pages and will serve to arouse in students a desire for further study.

CALVIN T. LONG
Pullman, Washington

Contents

Elementary Introduction to Number Theory

Preliminary Considerations

1.1 Introduction

Carl Friedrich Gauss (1777–1855), one of the greatest mathematicians, physicists, and astronomers of all time, once indicated his partiality for mathematics in general and for the theory of numbers in particular by remarking that "mathematics is the queen of the sciences, but number theory is the queen of mathematics." Today, with the obvious importance of mathematics as the principal tool in our breathtakingly rapid technological revolution, her queenship is more widely recognized than ever before.

It must not be supposed, however, that the sole function of mathematics is to be the servant of science or that her royal status depends only upon how well she serves. Quite the contrary, mathematics has a substance and beauty all its own which transcends any immediate use to which it may be put, and it is this quality that has continually attracted the attention of men like Gauss. To be sure, this quality is shared by other sciences as well, but it is particularly evident in the abstractions of mathematics. "A scientist worthy of the name," wrote Henri Poincaré (1854–1912), "above all a mathematician, experiences in his work the same sensations as an artist; his pleasure is as great and of the same nature." And W. F. White has written: "The beautiful has its place in mathematics for here are triumphs of the creative imagination, beautiful theorems, proofs and processes whose perfection of form has made them classic. He must be a 'practical' man who can see no poetry in mathematics."

Beauty, of course, is a matter of taste and it is not for anyone to determine the taste of another. Yet surprising results, economically stated and subtly proved have been a source of pleasure and satisfaction to the minds of men throughout the ages. Our hope for the reader is that he may derive a similar enjoyment from the reading of the following pages.

Not all of the succeeding theorems can appropriately be classed as beautiful nor are all of the proofs neat and elegant, but the theory of numbers has more than its fair share of such results and it is no doubt for this reason that Gauss characterized it as the "queen of mathematics." It *is* a fascinating study and we hope that as the reader penetrates into it more deeply, he too will be pleasantly surprised and pleased at the statement of a theorem or the turn of a proof. Even more, we hope that the reader may know the special pleasure of discovering and proving results for himself.

1

1.2 Summation and Multiplication Notation

From time to time as our development proceeds we shall have occasion to use special notation to simplify the writing of sums and products. The notation is standard but it may not be amiss to begin our study by reviewing its essential features.

Summation notation. For $r \leq s$, we use $\sum\limits_{i=r}^{s} a_i$ to represent the sum

$$a_r + a_{r+1} + \cdots + a_s;$$

s and r are called the *upper* and the *lower limits* of summation, and i is called the *index* of summation.

For example,

$$\sum_{i=0}^{4} a_i = a_0 + a_1 + a_2 + a_3 + a_4$$

and, analogously,

$$\sum_{j=1}^{3} j^2 = 1^2 + 2^2 + 3^2.$$

The idea is to replace the index of summation in the expression being summed by consecutive integers, starting with the lower limit of summation and stopping with the upper limit, and then to add the resulting expressions.

With this in mind, it is not difficult to derive a number of interesting results of a general nature. In each of the following cases, we shall use n and 1 for the upper and lower limits, but it is clear that any integers r and s, $r \leq s$, could be used just as well. First, we consider

$$(1) \qquad \sum_{i=1}^{n} a_i b_i = a_1 b_1 + a_2 b_2 + \cdots + a_n b_n.$$

If we set $b_i = k$ for $i = 1, 2, \ldots, n$ in (1), we obtain

$$(2) \qquad \sum_{i=1}^{n} k a_i = k \cdot \sum_{i=1}^{n} a_i.$$

This simply notes that a constant factor (independent of the index of summation) can be factored out of the entire summation. Moreover, if $a_i = 1$ as well as $b_i = k$ for each $i = 1, 2, \ldots, n$ in (1), we obtain

$$(2') \qquad \sum_{i=1}^{n} k = nk.$$

Thus, the summation of a constant (i.e., a quantity independent of the index of summation) is equal to the value of the constant times the *number* of values the index assumes. For example,

$$\sum_{i=5}^{17} 3 = 3 \cdot 13 = 39 \quad \text{and} \quad \sum_{j=0}^{5} 7b = 42b.$$

It is sometimes necessary to use multiple summation. If $k = b_j$ in (2), we have

$$(3) \qquad \sum_{i=1}^{n} a_i b_j = b_j \cdot \sum_{i=1}^{n} a_i,$$

and if we now sum both sides as j runs from 1 to m, we obtain

$$(4) \qquad \sum_{j=1}^{m} \sum_{i=1}^{n} a_i b_j = \sum_{j=1}^{m} \left(b_j \cdot \sum_{i=1}^{n} a_i \right).$$

Since, with regard to the summation on j, the entire sum $\sum_{i=1}^{n} a_i$ is constant, it follows from (2) that

$$(5) \qquad \sum_{j=1}^{m} \left(b_j \cdot \sum_{i=1}^{n} a_i \right) = \left(\sum_{j=1}^{m} b_j \right) \left(\sum_{i=1}^{n} a_i \right).$$

Combining this with (4), we obtain the very important result that

$$(6) \qquad \sum_{j=1}^{m} \sum_{i=1}^{n} a_i b_j = \sum_{j=1}^{m} b_j \cdot \sum_{i=1}^{n} a_i.$$

Here the parentheses are omitted since it is immaterial whether they appear as in the right side of (4) or the right side of (5).

Another important and useful summation formula is

$$
\begin{aligned}
\sum_{i=1}^{n} (a_i + b_i) &= (a_1 + b_1) + (a_2 + b_2) + \cdots + (a_n + b_n) \\
&= (a_1 + \cdots + a_n) + (b_1 + \cdots + b_n) \\
&= \sum_{i=1}^{n} a_i + \sum_{i=1}^{n} b_i.
\end{aligned}
$$

(7)

Multiplication notation. For $r \leq s$, we use

$$\prod_{i=r}^{s} a_i$$

to represent the product of the numbers $a_r, a_{r+1}, \ldots, a_s$.

For example,

$$\prod_{i=1}^{5} a_i = a_1 a_2 a_3 a_4 a_5$$

and

$$n! = \prod_{i=1}^{n} i.$$

As in the case of sums, it is possible to derive a number of useful formulas for special types of products. As before, we use n and 1 for upper and lower limits in the following products, but other limits could be used just as well. The derivations in each case are analogous to the ones for the corresponding sums. In the first place,

$$\prod_{i=1}^{n} a_i b_i = (a_1 b_1)(a_2 b_2) \cdots (a_n b_n)$$

(8)
$$= (a_1 a_2 \cdots a_n)(b_1 b_2 \cdots b_n)$$

$$= \prod_{i=1}^{n} a_i \cdot \prod_{i=1}^{n} b_i.$$

If we set $b_i = k$ for $i = 1, 2, \ldots, n$ in (8), we obtain

(9)
$$\prod_{i=1}^{n} k a_i = k^n \cdot \prod_{i=1}^{n} a_i,$$

which is frequently very useful. Moreover, if we set $a_i = 1$ for $i = 1, 2, \ldots, n$ in (9), we obtain

(10)
$$\prod_{i=1}^{n} k = k^n,$$

which says that the product of a constant is equal to the constant raised to a power equal to the number of values the index of multiplication assumes. For example, we note that

$$\prod_{i=1}^{n} i(i+1) = \prod_{i=1}^{n} i \cdot \prod_{i=1}^{n} (i+1)$$

$$= n!(n+1)!,$$

that

$$\prod_{i=1}^{n} 2i = 2^n \cdot n!,$$

and that

$$\prod_{i=1}^{n} 2 = 2^n.$$

One final result concerning products is suggested by (8). If $a_i = b_i$, then (8) becomes

$$\prod_{i=1}^{n} a_i^2 = \prod_{i=1}^{n} a_i \cdot \prod_{i=1}^{n} a_i = \left(\prod_{i=1}^{n} a_i \right)^2.$$

This suggests that, in general,

(11)
$$\prod_{i=1}^{n} a_i^k = \left(\prod_{i=1}^{n} a_i \right)^k.$$

The easy proof of this is left to the reader.

Exercises

1. Write out the following sums:

(a) $\displaystyle\sum_{i=1}^{5} (2i - 1)$

(b) $\displaystyle\sum_{i=0}^{6} \sin ix$

(c) $\displaystyle\sum_{j=1}^{n} \frac{2}{j(j + 1)}$

(d) $\displaystyle\sum_{k=5}^{10} 3$

2. Write the following in summation notation:

(a) $2 + 4 + 6 + 8 + 10$

(b) $1 + 8 + 27 + 64 + 125$

(c) $28 + 31 + 34 + 37 + 40 + 43$

(d) $n + (n + 2) + (n + 4) + \cdots + (n + 2m)$

3. Evaluate $\sum_{i=1}^{n} (a_i - a_{i-1})$ given that $a_0 = 0$.

4. Use the result of Exercise 3 to prove that $\sum_{i=1}^{n} i = n(n + 1)/2$.

5. Use the result of Exercise 3 to prove that $\sum_{i=1}^{n} i(i + 1) = n(n + 1)(n + 2)/3$.

6. Use the results of Exercises 4 and 5 to derive a formula for $\sum_{i=1}^{n} i^2$.

7. Write out the following products:

(a) $\displaystyle\prod_{j=1}^{4} (2j - 1)$

(b) $\displaystyle\prod_{j=0}^{5} \frac{j}{j + 1}$

(c) $\displaystyle\prod_{i=p}^{p+n} i$

8. Write the following in product notation:

(a) $2 \cdot 4 \cdot 6 \cdot 8 \cdot 10 \cdot 12$

(b) $(-1)^n \cdot n!$

(c) $\left(1 - \dfrac{1}{4}\right)\left(1 - \dfrac{1}{9}\right)\left(1 - \dfrac{1}{16}\right)\cdots\left(1 - \dfrac{1}{n^2}\right)$

9. Evaluate $\prod_{i=1}^{n} a^i$ and $\prod_{i=1}^{n} a^{i(i+1)}$.

10. Evaluate $\displaystyle\prod_{i=1}^{n} \frac{a_i}{a_{i-1}}$ given that $a_0 = 1$.

11. Use the result of Exercise 10 to prove that

$$\prod_{i=1}^{n} \left[1 - \frac{1}{(i + 1)^2}\right] = \frac{n + 2}{2(n + 1)}.$$

1.3 Postulates for the Positive Integers

Arithmetic, like the rest of mathematics, is a postulational system. It contains undefined terms, postulates or axioms concerning the undefined terms, defined terms, and theorems deduced as logical consequences of the postulates. The positive integers themselves, together with the operations of addition and multiplication and the relation of equality, may be taken as the undefined terms of arithmetic and the following statements may be taken as postulates.

Closure laws. If a and b are any two positive integers, there exist unique positive integers c and d such that $a + b = c$ and $ab = d$.

Commutative laws. If a and b are any two positive integers, then
$$a + b = b + a \text{ and } ab = ba.$$

Associative laws. If a, b, and c are any three positive integers, then
$$(a + b) + c = a + (b + c) \text{ and } (ab)c = a(bc).$$

Distributive law. If a, b, and c are any three positive integers, then
$$a(b + c) = ab + ac.$$

Cancellation law for addition. If a, b, and c are three positive integers with $a + b = a + c$, then $b = c$.

Cancellation law for multiplication. If a, b, and c are three positive integers with $ab = ac$, then $b = c$.

Multiplicative identity. There exists a positive integer designated by the symbol "1" having the property that $1 \cdot a = a$ for every positive integer a.

Law of trichotomy. If a and b are any two positive integers, then precisely one of the following holds: either $a = b$, or $a < b$, or $a > b$; i.e. either $a = b$, or $a + c = b$, or $a = b + d$ where c and d are positive integers.

One additional postulate, which must be assumed in one form or another and which is often misunderstood, is the so-called *principle of mathematical induction* or its equivalent, the *well-ordering principle*. We list three alternative statements.

I_1. **First form of the principle of mathematical induction.** Any set of positive integers which contains the integer 1 and which contains $k + 1$ whenever it contains the positive integer k, contains all positive integers.

I_2. **Second form of the principle of mathematical induction.** Any set of positive integers which contains the integer 1 and which contains $k + 1$ whenever it contains the positive integers $1, 2, \ldots, k$, contains all positive integers.

I_3. **The well-ordering principle.** Every nonempty set of positive integers contains a least element.

The reader should bear in mind that one or another of these principles must be taken as a postulate for the system of positive integers, and we shall show that the other two can then be proved as theorems. Thus, all three hold for the set of positive integers. What do they tell us about the system of positive integers and how can we make use of this information?

In effect, the first form of the principle of mathematical induction, I_1, simply says that the set of all positive integers can be generated by starting with 1, and adding 1 successively *ad infinitum*, i.e., that the infinite sequence 1, $1 + 1 = 2$, $2 + 1 = 3$, $3 + 1 = 4, \ldots$ contains all positive integers. The reader should note that this is said in I_1 by giving two conditions which guarantee that a set of positive integers is the set of all positive integers. The first condition specifies that the integer 1 be in the set, while the second condition states that if any particular integer is in the set, then so is its successor. But if 1 is in the set and the successor to 1 is in the set, then 2 is in the set. And if 2 is in the set, then so is 3, and so on. Thus we have an infinite sequence which contains all the positive integers.

The second form of the principle of mathematical induction, I_2, says the same thing about the system of positive integers as does I_1, but in a slightly different way. Again, there are two conditions which guarantee that a set of positive integers is the set of all positive integers. This time, however, the second condition states that if all positive integers from 1 up to and including any given integer are in the set, then the successor to that integer is also in the set. The first condition, as before, specifies that 1 be in the set. Taken together, these conditions imply that 2 is in the set. But then 1 and 2 are in the set and so 3 is in the set, and so on, as before.

Finally, the well-ordering principle, I_3, guarantees that if one has a set actually containing positive integers and only positive integers, then the set contains a smallest member. At first thought, it might seem that this would be true of any nonempty set of numbers, but this is not the case. For example, the set of positive real numbers fails to have a least element and so does the set of negative integers.

As noted earlier, it is not difficult to show that these three principles are equivalent, but first it may be worthwhile to see how they can be used in the formulation of proofs.

1.4 Mathematical Induction

We may illustrate the use of I_1 by assuming it as a postulate and using it to prove the following theorem:

Theorem 1.1. *For every positive integer n, $\sum_{i=1}^{n} i = n(n + 1)/2$.*

PROOF. Let C be the set of all positive integral values of n for which the formula of the theorem is true. Clearly, 1 is in C since, for $n = 1$, the assertion is simply that $1 = 1(1 + 1)/2$. Now suppose that k is in C where k is a fixed but unspecified positive integer; i.e., suppose that $1 + 2 + \cdots + k = k(k+1)/2$. Then

$$1 + 2 + \cdots + k + (k + 1) = \frac{k(k + 1)}{2} + (k + 1)$$

$$= \frac{k(k + 1)}{2} + \frac{2(k + 1)}{2}$$

$$= \frac{(k + 1)(k + 2)}{2}.$$

Thus, if the formula is true for $n = k$, it is also true for $n = k + 1$; so $k + 1$ is in C if k is in C. Finally, since C satisfies both conditions of I_1, it must contain all positive integers. Hence, the given formula is true for all positive integers n as claimed.

Of course, one does not usually frame a proof based on I_1 (such proofs are called proofs by mathematical induction as are those based on I_2) in terms of a set C, as in the preceding argument. It was done here only to make its dependence on I_1 completely clear. The essential features of the proof are that one must show that (step one) the result in question holds for $n = 1$ and that (step two) it holds for $n = k + 1$ whenever it holds for $n = k$, and this is all that is usually written down. Thus, for example, the preceding proof would more often be written in the following more abbreviated form.

PROOF. For $n = 1$, the assertion of the theorem is clearly true. Now, assume that $\sum_{i=1}^{k} i = k(k + 1)/2$ where k is any fixed but unspecified positive integer. Then

$$\sum_{i=1}^{k+1} i = \frac{k(k + 1)}{2} + (k + 1) = \frac{(k + 1)(k + 2)}{2}$$

Thus, since the assertion is true for $n = k + 1$ if it is true for $n = k$, it is true for every positive integer n by the principle of mathematical induction.

The reader should note that *both* steps in a proof based on I_1 must be carried out before the desired conclusion can be drawn. For example, step one can be completed for the false formula

$$\sum_{i=1}^{n} i = \frac{n(n + 1)}{2} + (n - 1),$$

while step two cannot, and step two can be completed for the false formula

$$\sum_{i=1}^{n} i = \frac{n(n + 1)}{2} + 5,$$

while step one cannot. Step two of the proof shows, essentially, that if the desired result is true for any given integer, then it is also true for the next. Thus, if the result has been shown to be true for $n = 1$, it must also be true for $n = 2$. And, since it is then true for $n = 2$, it must be true also for $n = 3$, and so on.

One must also be sure that the argument made in step two of the proof does not depend on any particular value of k. The argument must hold for *any* fixed but unspecified positive integer k or else the "and so on" of the preceding paragraph will break down. For example, let us "prove" that all positive integers are equal. The statement "any n positive integers are equal" is certainly true in case $n = 1$. Let us now assume it to be true for $n = k$ and prove that it must, therefore, be true for $n = k + 1$. Let

$$\overbrace{a_1, \underbrace{a_2, a_3, \ldots, a_k, a_{k+1}}}$$

be any $k + 1$ positive integers. By assumption, the first k must be equal and also the last k must be equal, as indicated above by the braces. But then, because of the overlap, it is apparent that all of the numbers must be equal. Thus, the assertion is true for $n = k + 1$ if it is true for $n = k$ and the "proof" is complete. The difficulty, of course, is that there is no overlap between the first k numbers and the last k numbers in the above diagram in case $k = 1$. Thus, step two of the argument is valid only for $k \geq 2$ and cannot be used to conclude that the result claimed is true for $n = 2$ if it is true for $n = 1$. However, it might be noted that if a separate argument could be given to prove the validity of the assertion for $n = 2$, then step two could be used to extend the result upwards from 2.

The preceding remark suggests that the method of proof based on I_1 can be modified to prove that a result is true for all integers greater than or equal to any fixed integer, so that the induction does not have to begin with $n = 1$. For example, if one wanted to prove that a result were true for all integers greater than or equal to 29, it would suffice to prove it for $n = 29$ and for $n = k + 1$ on the basis of the assumption of its truth for $n = k$, where k is any fixed but unspecified integer greater than or equal to 29 (see Exercise 16 below).

A proof based on I_2 is exactly like one based on I_1, with one exception. In step two of the proof, one assumes the truth of the assertion for all values of n from 1 to k inclusive and, on the basis of this assumption, must then prove its truth for $n = k + 1$. The point is that the truth of the $(k + 1)$st case often does not follow directly from the truth of the kth case, but does follow from the truth of the assertion for some or all of the positive integers preceding $k + 1$. Even in such cases, it is possible (by a devious trick) to use I_1, but a proof based on I_2 would be much more natural.

Before giving an example of such a situation, we note that the same general remarks apply to proofs based on I_2 as to those based on I_1. By this we mean that both steps of the proof must be carried out before the conclusion can be drawn, and that the argument in the second step of the proof must not depend on any particular value of k. Also, as indicated in the discussion of I_1, the induction can begin with 2, or 29, or any other integer in place of 1. For example, if 2 were used in place of 1, this would amount to saying that I_2 could be modified to read as follows: Any set of integers not less than 2 which contains 2 and contains $k + 1$ whenever it contains the integers $2, 3, \ldots, k$, contains all integers not less than 2 (see Exercise 17 below). We mention this case in particular since one of the simplest examples of a result which lends itself in a natural way to proof based on I_1 is a theorem true for all integers not less than 2 to which I_2, without this modification, would not apply. Before discussing this theorem, it will be necessary to introduce some terminology.

Definition 1.1. If a and b are integers with $a \neq 0$ and there exists an integer c such that $b = ac$, then we say that a *divides* b and write $a \mid b$. We also call a a *divisor* of b and b a *multiple* of a. If $1 \leq a < b$ and $a \mid b$, then a is called a *proper divisor* of b. If a does not divide b, we write $a \nmid b$.

Definition 1.2. If p is an integer greater than 1 whose only positive divisors are 1 and p itself, then p is called a *prime*. If p exceeds 1 and is not a prime, then it is called *composite*.

As examples of these definitions, we note that 1, 2, 3, and 6 are all divisors of 6, and all but 6 are proper divisors. Also, 2 and 3 are primes and 6 is composite. The integer 1 is neither prime nor composite.

We now illustrate the method of proof based on I_2. Note that we assume I_2 as modified as a postulate and prove the theorem in the simplified form without introducing a set C as in the first proof of Theorem 1.1.

Theorem 1.2. *Every integer $n \geq 2$ is either a prime or can be represented as a product of primes.*

PROOF. The assertion is trivially true for $n = 2$ since 2 is a prime. Assume that it is true for $n = 2, 3, \ldots, k$ where k is any fixed but unspecified integer not less than 2. We must show that on the basis of this assumption, the assertion of the theorem is also true for $n = k + 1$. If $k + 1$ is a prime, there is nothing to show. If $k + 1$ is composite, then there exist integers r and s with $2 \leq r \leq k$ and $2 \leq s \leq k$ such that $k + 1 = rs$. Since r and s both lie between 2 and k, we have, by assumption, that both are either primes or products of primes. Therefore, in this case, $k + 1$ must be a product of at least two primes. In any case, $k + 1$ is a prime or a product of primes and the assertion of the theorem is true for $n = k + 1$ if it is true for $n = 2, 3, \ldots, k$. Thus, by I_2 as modified, it is true for all $n \geq 2$.

The reader should observe that the second part of the preceding proof depended upon knowing that the assertion of the theorem held for both r and s. Since we knew only that r and s lay somewhere between 2 and k it was necessary to assume that the assertion of the theorem held for all integers in this range. Using I_1 in a natural way and making the induction assumption only for $n = k$ would not have sufficed.

Exercises

1. Prove that $\displaystyle\sum_{i=1}^{n} \frac{1}{i(i+1)} = \frac{n}{n+1}$ for every positive integer n.

2. Prove that $\displaystyle\sum_{i=1}^{n} i^3 = \frac{n^2(n+1)^2}{4}$ for every positive integer n.

3. Use I_1 to prove that $2^{2n} - 1$ is divisible by 3 for every positive integer n.

4. Prove that $2^{2n-1} + 1$ is divisible by 3 for every positive integer n.

5. Prove that $f(n) = 3n^5 + 5n^3 + 7n$ is divisible by 15 for *every* integer n. *Hint:* Note that $f(-n) = -f(n)$.

6. Prove that $3^{2n+1} + 2^{n+2}$ is divisible by 7 for every nonnegative integer n.

The *Fibonacci sequence*, named after Leonardo of Pisa (1170?–1250?) who was nicknamed Fibonacci, is defined by the equations $f_1 = 1$, $f_2 = 1$, and $f_n = f_{n-1} + f_{n-2}$ for $n \geq 3$. This sequence, whose first few terms are 1, 1, 2, 3, 5, 8, 13, 21, $\ldots$, has many remarkable properties, a goodly number of which can be proved by mathematical induction. Moreover, it is not difficult to discover many of these relations by simply considering a number of examples, much as a physicist might go about discovering a physical law.

For example, if we write the sums of successive Fibonacci numbers

$$1 = 1$$
$$1 + 1 = 2$$
$$1 + 1 + 2 = 4$$
$$1 + 1 + 2 + 3 = 7$$
$$1 + 1 + 2 + 3 + 5 = 12$$

. . . .

and note also that the numbers on the right are each one smaller than a Fibonacci number, we are not far from guessing that

$$\sum_{i=1}^{n} f_i = f_{n+2} - 1$$

for every positive integer n. A number of problems of this sort are given below. We hope that they provide some small pleasure to the reader.

Incidentally, the inductive approach, that of considering examples and trying to guess general laws, is quite productive in all of mathematics and particularly in the theory of numbers. This is so much the case that Euler (1707–1783) once wrote, "... as I shall show here with very good reasons, the properties of the numbers known today have been mostly discovered by observation, and discovered long before their truth has been confirmed by rigid demonstrations. There are even many properties of the numbers with which we are well acquainted but which we are not yet able to prove; only observations have led us to their knowledge. Hence we see that in the theory of numbers, which is still very imperfect, we can place our highest hopes in observations; they will lead us continually to new properties which we shall endeavor to prove afterwards."

7. Prove that $\sum_{i=1}^{n} f_i = f_{n+2} - 1$ for every positive integer n.

8. Discover formulas for each of the following sums and prove that each is correct for every positive integer n:

(a) $\displaystyle\sum_{i=1}^{n} f_{2i-1}$

(b) $\displaystyle\sum_{i=1}^{n} f_{2i}$

(c) $\displaystyle\sum_{i=1}^{n} (-1)^{i-1} f_i$

(d) $\displaystyle\sum_{i=1}^{2n-1} f_i f_{i+1}$

9. Prove that $\sum_{i=1}^{n} f_i^2 = f_n f_{n+1}$ for every positive integer n.

10. Let $\alpha = (1 + \sqrt{5})/2$ and $\beta = (1 - \sqrt{5})/2$ so that α and β are the roots of $x^2 = x + 1$. Use I_2 to prove that $f_n = (\alpha^n - \beta^n)/\sqrt{5}$. Note that, in this case, it is necessary to make the first part of the proof for $n = 2$ as well as for $n = 1$. Why? This formula is due to Binet.

11. Use I_2 to prove that $\alpha^{n-2} \leq f_n \leq \alpha^{n-1}$ for every positive integer n. Note that it is again necessary to make the first part of the proof for $n = 1$ and $n = 2$.

12. Prove that $\alpha^n = f_{n-1} + \alpha f_n$ for $n \geq 1$, provided we define $f_0 = 0$.

13. Prove that $f_{n+m+1} = f_n f_m + f_{n+1} f_{m+1}$ for $m \geq 0$, $n \geq 0$. *Hint:* Hold m constant and use induction on n.

14. Deduce from Exercise 13 that f_n divides f_{2n} for every $n \geq 1$.

15. Prove that f_n divides f_{mn} for $n \geq 1$, $m \geq 1$.

16. On the basis of I_1, as stated on page 6, prove the following slightly more general assertion. If a is an integer and A is a set of integers none of which is less than a and which contains a and contains $k + 1$ whenever it contains k where k is any fixed but unspecified integer not less than a, then A contains all integers not less than a. *Hint:* Let Q_n be the statement "$a + n - 1$ is an element of A" and use I_1 to prove that Q_n is true for all $n \geq 1$.

17. On the basis of I_2 as stated on page 6, prove the following slightly more general assertion. If a is an integer and A is a set of integers none of which is less than a and which contains a and contains $k + 1$ whenever it contains a, $a + 1, \ldots, k$ where k is any fixed but unspecified integer not less than a, then A contains all integers not less than a.

1.5 The Well-Ordering Principle

We now illustrate the method of proof based on the well-ordering principle, I_3, by proving the following little result concerning the number 1.

Theorem 1.3. *If a is a positive integer, then $a \geq 1$; i.e., 1 is the least positive integer.*

PROOF. Suppose, on the contrary, that there exists an integer a such that $0 < a < 1$. Then, if C is the set of such integers, it is not empty. Therefore, by I_3, C must have a least element. Let b be the least element of C. Then $0 < b < 1$ and, on multiplication by b, $0 < b^2 < b$. But then b^2 is an element of C which is smaller than b and this contradicts the fact that b was the least element of C. Because of this contradiction, our original assumption must be false, so that $a \geq 1$ for every positive integer a.

As in this case, many proofs based on the well-ordering principle involve the method of proof by contradiction. To prove a theorem by contradiction, one proceeds, in general, as follows. One begins by assuming that the theorem is false, and then one deduces from this assumption a result which is *known* to be false, or which contradicts the primary assumption. We shall have many occasions in the discussions which follow to use this method of proof.

The preceding proof also provides an easy illustration of the method of proof due to P. Fermat (1601–1665) and known as *Fermat's method of infinite descent*. In general, such a proof has the following form. One assumes that there is a positive integer r possessing some property P. One then deduces that there is some positive integer $s < r$ which also has property P. But, since this argument could be repeated *ad infinitum*, it contradicts the fact that there must be a smallest positive integer with property P. Hence, there must be no positive integer possessing property P.

Finally, it should be observed that the well-ordering principle can be generalized along the same lines as I_1 and I_2. For example, it could be shown from the well-ordering principle as stated that any nonempty set of integers, none of which is less than some fixed integer b, has a least element. Also, one could prove that any nonempty set of integers, none of which is greater than some fixed integer c, has a greatest element.

Exercises

1. Use the method of proof by contradiction to show that if r is a real number and r^2 is irrational, then r is irrational. *Hint:* Recall that an irrational number is a real number which cannot be expressed as the quotient of two integers.

2. The Archimedean axiom states that if a and b are positive integers, there exists an integer n such that $an \geq b$. Use the well-ordering principle to prove that this is so. *Hint:* Suppose the assertion is false and consider the set C of all positive integers of the form $b - na$.

3. Use the well-ordering principle as stated to prove that any nonempty set C of integers none of which is less than a specified integer a has a least element. *Hint:* Consider the set D of all integers of the form $c - a + 1$ where c is an element of C.

1.6 Equivalence of the Principles of Induction and Well-Ordering

In this section we show that in the presence of the other postulates for the positive integers, I_1, I_2, and I_3 are equivalent.

Theorem 1.4. I_1 *implies* I_2.

PROOF. We take I_1 as a postulate and must prove I_2 as a theorem. Let C be any set of positive integers satisfying the conditions of I_2. The problem is to show that C contains all positive integers.

Let A_n denote the statement "the integers 1 to n inclusive are in C." A_1 is true by hypothesis. Now, assume that A_k is true where k is any fixed but unspecified positive integer. Then 1 to k inclusive are in C. Hence, again by hypothesis, $k + 1$ is in C and A_{k+1} is true. Therefore, by I_1, A_n is true for every integer $n \geq 1$ and so C contains all positive integers.

Theorem 1.5. I_2 *implies* I_3.

PROOF. We now take I_2 as a postulate and prove I_3 as a theorem. Let C be a nonempty set of positive integers. We must show that C has a least element. Since $1 \geq 1$ and $k + 1 > k \geq 1$ if $k \geq 1$, we have by I_2 that 1 is the least positive integer. Assume that C has no least element and let A_n denote the statement "n is not an element of C." A_1 is true, for otherwise C would have 1 as a least element. Assume that $A_1, \ldots, A_k$ are all true. Then A_{k+1} must also be true, for otherwise $k + 1$ would be the least element in C. Thus, by I_2, A_n is true for every positive integer n. But this implies that C is empty, contrary to hypothesis. Therefore, the assumption that C has no least element is false and the theorem is proved.

Theorem 1.6. I_3 *implies* I_1.

PROOF. Let C be a set of positive integers satisfying the conditions of I_1. Assuming I_3 as a postulate, we must prove that C contains all positive integers.

Suppose that C does not contain all positive integers. Then the set C^* of all positive integers not in C is nonempty. Therefore, by I_3, C^* has a least element. It follows from Theorem 1.3, which we proved by using I_3, that no elements of C^* are less than 1 and, hence, that the least element of C^* is not less than 1. Moreover, the least element of C^* cannot be 1 since, by hypothesis, 1 is in C. Thus, the least element in C^* can be written in the form $k + 1$ where k is a positive integer. But this says that k is in C while $k + 1$ is not, in direct contradiction to the hypotheses. Thus, the assumption that C does not contain all positive integers is false and the theorem is proved.

The preceding theorems show that I_1 implies I_2, that I_2 implies I_3, and that I_3 implies I_1. Thus, if any of these propositions is assumed as a postulate for the positive integers, the others are immediately available as theorems. We shall have a number of occasions to use each of these principles in what follows.

1.7 The Division Algorithm

In order to simplify notation here and throughout the remainder of the book, we shall always use lower case italic letters to denote integers unless explicitly stated to the contrary.

Theorem 1.7 (The Division Algorithm). *For any $b > 0$ and a, there exist unique integers q and r with $0 \leq r < b$ such that $a = bq + r$.*

PROOF. The proof depends on the modification of the well-ordering principle discussed on page 13.

Let C be the set of all nonnegative integers of the form $a - sb$. If $a \geq 0$, then $a - 0b$ is an element of C. If $a < 0$, then $a - ab = a(1 - b) \geq 0$ is an element of C since $b \geq 1$. Thus, in either case, C is not empty. Hence, by the well-ordering principle, C has a least element. Let q denote that value of s which yields the least element of C and set $a - bq = r$. Thus, since r is the least nonnegative element of this form, it follows that $0 \leq r$ and

$$r - b = a - bq - b = a - (q + 1) \cdot b < 0,$$

so that $0 \leq r < b$ as claimed.

The first part of the proof has shown that q and r with the desired properties must exist. To show that q and r are unique, we must show that they are the *only* integers with the desired properties. Suppose that $a = bq' + r'$ where $0 \leq r' < b$. It suffices to show that $r = r'$ and $q = q'$. If $q' < q$, then $q' + 1 \leq q$ since q and q' are both integers. Therefore,

$$r = a - bq \leq a - b(q' + 1) = a - bq' - b = r' - b < 0$$

and this is a contradiction. Similarly, we obtain a contradiction if $q' > q$.

Thus, it must be the case that $q = q'$. But then, $bq + r = a = bq + r'$ and so $r = r'$ as well.

Stated somewhat differently, this theorem simply says that if one divides a by the positive integer b, one obtains a quotient q and a remainder r where r is nonnegative and less than b. However, the restriction that b be positive is not strictly necessary, and the theorem could also be written in the form: given integers a and b with $b \neq 0$, there exist unique integers q and r with $0 \leq r < |b|$ such that $a = bq + r$.

The division algorithm is surprisingly useful as we shall see subsequently. As a first example, note that with $b = 2$, the theorem implies that every integer a is either of the form $2k$ or of the form $2k + 1$ (i.e., even or odd). Then, a^2 is either of the form $4k^2 = 4r$ or $4k^2 + 4k + 1 = 4s + 1$. Hence, the square of an integer must leave a remainder of 0 or 1 when divided by 4; it cannot leave a remainder of 2 or 3. Similarly, any integer a must be of the form $3k$, or $3k + 1$, or $3k + 2$. Thus, a^2 must be of the form $9k^2 = 3u$, or $9k^2 + 6k + 1 = 3v + 1$, or $9k^2 + 12k + 4 = 3w + 1$. Hence, the square of an integer must leave a remainder of 0 or 1 when divided by 3; it cannot leave a remainder of 2. Admittedly, these are only small results, but they are not without interest and they indicate an important way in which the division algorithm can be used.

Exercises

1. Prove that no number in the sequence $11, 111, 1111, 11111, \ldots$, is a perfect square.

2. If p is a prime other than 2 or 5, prove that p must be one of the forms $10k + 1$, $10k + 3$, $10k + 7$, or $10k + 9$.

3. Prove that the product of any two odd numbers must be odd.

4. Prove that one of any two consecutive integers must be even.

5. Prove that one of any three consecutive integers must be divisible by 3.

6. If a is an integer, prove that one of the numbers a, $a + 2$, and $a + 4$ is divisible by 3.

7. If n is an integer not divisible by 2 or 3, show that $n^2 + 23$ must be divisible by 24. *Hint:* Any integer must be of the form $6k$, $6k + 1, \ldots$, or $6k + 5$.

8. If a, b, and c are integers with $a^2 + b^2 = c^2$, show that a and b cannot both be odd.

9. If a and b are integers with $b < 0$, prove that there exist unique integers q and r with $0 \leq r < |b|$ such that $a = bq + r$.

1.8 Positional Notation

For many theoretical purposes in the theory of numbers it is immaterial what system one uses for the representation of numbers. The Greeks, for example, with a very cumbersome notation, were able to discover and prove many basic properties of the integers. For practical purposes, however, and for theoretical matters requiring detailed computation, it is important to have a notation which facilitates calculation. The Hindu-Arabic system of notation, in worldwide use today, certainly meets this requirement and, while it is well known from constant usage, it may not be amiss to discuss it here in some detail.

In the first place, the Hindu-Arabic system is a *positional* system of notation. For example, we write 2922 as shorthand for the much more cumbersome expression $2 \cdot 10^3 + 9 \cdot 10^2 + 2 \cdot 10 + 2$ and let the position of each *digit* determine its contribution to the total value of the number being represented. Thus, the three twos above contribute, respectively, two thousand, twenty, and two and the nine contributes nine hundred to the total value of two thousand nine hundred twenty-two.

In the second place, the Hindu-Arabic system is said to have the *base* 10, since all numbers are expressed as sums of multiples of powers of 10, as in the preceding example. Incidentally, it is not difficult to imagine how this all came about. Members of the human race normally come equipped with built-in calculators with ten keys and, quite naturally, count large numbers by repeatedly counting the ten fingers. Indeed, the numbers we use as multipliers of the powers of ten in our present system are called digits, as are the fingers and toes.

The great power of this system of notation is that any integer, however large, can be conveniently represented by repeated use of only 10 symbols and that simple algorithms, or orderly methods of computation, can be devised for carrying out arithmetical computations. Other systems, like the Roman, for example, require the creation of more and more symbols for the representation of ever larger numbers, and even such simple operations as addition and multiplication are quite tedious, to say nothing about division or root extraction.

For example,

$$\begin{aligned} \text{XXVIII} + \text{XXXIV} &= \text{XXVIII} + \text{XXXIIII} \\ &= \text{XXXXXVIIIIIII} \\ &= \text{LVVII} \\ &= \text{LXII} \end{aligned}$$

and

$$\begin{aligned} (\text{XIX}) \cdot (\text{II}) &= (\text{XVIIII}) \cdot (\text{II}) \\ &= \text{XVIIII} + \text{XVIIII} \\ &= \text{XXVVIIIIIIII} \\ &= \text{XXXVIII}. \end{aligned}$$

One needs only to compare these calculations with the corresponding ones using ordinary base 10 arithmetic to appreciate the advantage positional notation affords. The usual simple rules for borrowing and carrying in subtraction and addition, as well as the methods for multiplication, division, and root extraction, depend entirely on this notion.

The following theorem shows that it is always possible to represent an integer in decimal form and also suggests some interesting alternatives.

Theorem 1.8. *Let b be greater than 1. Then, every $a > 0$ can be uniquely represented in the form*

$$a = c_n b^n + c_{n-1} b^{n-1} + \cdots + c_1 b + c_0$$

with $c_n \neq 0$, $n \geq 0$, and $0 \leq c_i < b$ for $i = 0, 1, 2, \ldots, n$.

PROOF. We first show that every $a > 0$ has a representation of the desired form and then show that the representations are unique.

(i) For $a = 1$, it suffices to take $n = 0$, $c_0 = 1$.

(ii) Assume that every integer from 1 to k inclusive can be represented in the desired way. On the basis of this assumption, it must be shown that $k + 1$ can also be represented in this way. By Theorem 1.7, there exist integers c_0 and q with $0 \leq c_0 < b$ such that $k + 1 = bq + c_0$. If $q = 0$, then $c_0 \neq 0$ and $k + 1 = c_0$ so that $k + 1$ is represented in the desired form. If $q > 0$, then $q = (k + 1 - c_0)/b \leq (k + 1)/2 \leq k$, since $b \geq 2$ and $k \geq 1$. Thus, by the induction assumption, q can be represented in the desired way; i.e., there exist constants which we may denote by $c_1, c_2, \ldots, c_m$ with $c_m \neq 0$ and $0 \leq c_i < b$ for $i = 1, 2, \ldots, m$ such that

$$q = c_m b^{m-1} + c_{m-1} b^{m-2} + \cdots + c_2 b + c_1.$$

Hence,

$$k + 1 = bq + c_0 = c_m b^m + \cdots + c_1 b + c_0$$

and so can be represented in the desired way. Thus, by mathematical induction, every positive integer a can be represented in this way.

(iii) We must still show that the representation of each integer a is unique. Suppose that some a can be represented in two essentially different ways, say

$$a = c_0 + c_1 b + \cdots + c_n b^n$$
$$= d_0 + d_1 b + \cdots + d_m b^m$$

with $c_n \neq 0$, $d_m \neq 0$, $0 \leq c_i < b$ for each i, $0 \leq d_j < b$ for each j, and with $m \geq n$. Then by subtraction,

$$0 = e_0 + e_1 b + \cdots + e_m b^m$$

where $e_i = d_i - c_i$ for $i = 0, \ldots, n$, $e_i = d_i$ for $i = n+1, \ldots, m$ if $m > n$. In view of the inequalities on the c's and d's it follows that $-(b - 1) \leq e_i \leq (b - 1)$ for each i. Also, $e_i \neq 0$ for some i since we assumed that the two representations for a were essentially different. Let e_k be the nonzero e with the largest subscript. Then,

$$-e_k b^k = e_0 + e_1 b + \cdots + e_{k-1} b^{k-1}$$

and

$$b^k \leq |-e_k b^k| = |e_0 + e_1 b + \cdots + e_{k-1} b^{k-1}|$$
$$\leq |e_0| + |e_1| b + \cdots + |e_{k-1}| b^{k-1}$$
$$\leq (b - 1) + (b - 1)b + \cdots + (b - 1)b^{k-1} = b^k - 1.$$

Since this is a clear contradiction, it must be the case that $m = n$ and $c_i = d_i$ for all i. Thus, the representation is unique.

Theorem 1.8 shows that positional representation of numbers is possible with any integer $b > 1$ as base. For example, if $b = 8$, Theorem 1.8 guarantees that any positive integer can be written uniquely as a sum of multiples of powers of 8 where the multipliers come from among the integers 0 through 7. Thus, one hundred thirty-one can be written as $2 \cdot 8^2 + 0 \cdot 8 + 3$ and, just as the representations of integers as sums of multiples of powers of ten are abbreviated to decimal notation, this might be abbreviated in *octal* notation to 203. Indeed, this is almost certainly the way the number would have been written if men had been equipped with four digits instead of five on each hand. In order to avoid confusion, we shall frequently use a subscript, written in base ten notation, to indicate the base. For the example above, we have that $131_{10} = 203_8$. Incidentally, 203_8 should be read "two zero three, base eight" and not "two hundred three" since our language for numbers is already oriented to base ten.

Since our rules for numerical computation depend on the positional character of decimal notation and not on the base, calculations with numbers written in octal notation would be carried out as usual except that we would have to use different addition and multiplication tables, as shown below.

ADDITION AND MULTIPLICATION TABLES FOR BASE EIGHT

+	1	2	3	4	5	6	7
1	2	3	4	5	6	7	10
2	3	4	5	6	7	10	11
3	4	5	6	7	10	11	12
4	5	6	7	10	11	12	13
5	6	7	10	11	12	13	14
6	7	10	11	12	13	14	15
7	10	11	12	13	14	15	16

×	1	2	3	4	5	6	7
1	1	2	3	4	5	6	7
2	2	4	6	10	12	14	16
3	3	6	11	14	17	22	25
4	4	10	14	20	24	30	34
5	5	12	17	24	31	36	43
6	6	14	22	30	36	44	52
7	7	16	25	34	43	52	61

For example, the product of twenty-five and twenty would be found, in base eight, as follows:

$$
\begin{array}{r}
31 \\
24 \\
\hline
144 \\
62 \\
\hline
764
\end{array}
$$

Thus, $764_8 = 7 \cdot 8^2 + 6 \cdot 8 + 4 = 500_{10}$. Similarly, the sum of thirty-five and thirty would appear in octal notation as

$$
\begin{array}{r}
1 \\
43 \\
36 \\
\hline
101
\end{array}
$$

and $101_8 = 1 \cdot 8^2 + 0 \cdot 8 + 1 = 65_{10}$ as it should. The reader should work through these calculations with the help of the above tables to see what is involved at each step.

A recent application is the use of base two in connection with the modern electronic computing machines. This is particularly appropriate since in base two only the digits 0 and 1 are required, and these can easily be expressed in the machine by a switch being either on or off, a spot on a magnetic tape being magnetized or not magnetized, a spot on the face of an electrostatic tube being either charged or not charged, and so on. Of course, arithmetic to base two is greatly simplified since one need only learn the addition and multiplication tables through the ones. For example, multiplying eleven by seven in base two, one would have:

$$
\begin{array}{r}
1011 \\
111 \\
\hline
1011 \\
1011 \\
1011 \\
\hline
1001101
\end{array}
$$

Sixty is divided by ten as follows:

$$
\begin{array}{r}
110 \\
1010 \overline{)111100} \\
1010 \\
\hline
1010 \\
1010 \\
\hline
\end{array}
$$

The reader should check to see that all of these calculations are correct.

Now, it happens that there is a very simple method for obtaining the positional representation of any positive integer a to any base $b > 1$. By Theorem 1.7, we are assured that there exist integers q_1 and r_1 such that $a = bq_1 + r_1$ and $0 \leq r_1 < b$. Also, there exist q_2 and r_2 such that $q_1 = bq_2 + r_2$ with $0 \leq r_2 < b$. Again, there exists q_3 and r_3 such that $q_2 = bq_3 + r_3$ with $0 \leq r_3 < b$, and so on. Now, it is clear that $a > q_1 > q_2 > q_3 > \cdots$. Thus, we must finally reach the place where some q is smaller than b though still positive; that is, for some k, $0 < q_k < b$. If we divide once more by b, we obtain $q_k = 0 \cdot b + r_{k+1}$ with $0 < r_{k+1} < b$ and this ends the process. Now,

$$
\begin{aligned}
a &= bq_1 + r_1 \\
&= b(bq_2 + r_2) + r_1 = b^2 q_2 + br_2 + r_1 \\
&= b^2(bq_3 + r_3) + br_2 + r_1 = b^3 q_3 + b^2 r_3 + br_2 + r_1 \\
&= \cdots \\
&= b^k r_{k+1} + b^{k-1} r_k + \cdots + br_2 + r_1
\end{aligned}
$$

which is a representation of a in the form described in Theorem 1.8. But, since a is *uniquely* expressible in this form, this must be *the* desired representation.

For example, if we want to write 356_{10} in positional notation to base seven, we perform the successive divisions as follows:

$$7\underline{|356}$$
$$7\underline{|50} = q_1, r_1 = 6$$
$$7\underline{|7} = q_2, r_2 = 1$$
$$7\underline{|1} = q_3, r_3 = 0$$
$$0 = q_4, r_4 = 1$$

Thus, $356_{10} = 1016_7$.

Exercises

1. Express 247_{10} to base 7, base 2, and base 12 (using t and e for the digits ten and eleven in base 12).

2. What number to base 10 is represented by 324_6? by 324_{12}? by 10_7? by 10_5? by 100_6?

3. What number to base 10 is represented by 21.7_8? (This has not been discussed, but the extension should be clear.)

4. Carry out the following computations using octal notation throughout. Check your work by converting to decimal notation:
   (a) $257_8 + 361_8$ (b) $257_8 \times 361_8$
   (c) $361_8 - 257_8$ (d) $1356_8 \div 31_8$

5. Construct addition and multiplication tables for base 5 and in that base carry out the following calculations:
   (a) $423_5 + 242_5$ (b) $423_5 \times 242_5$
   (c) $331_5 \div 23_5$ (d) $\sqrt{313104_5}$

Divisibility Properties
of Integers

2.1 Basic Properties

Among the most important ideas in the theory of numbers is that of the divisibility of integers; we introduced this concept in Definitions 1.1 and 1.2. Questions concerning primes and divisors were among the earliest to be considered when man first began to reflect on the properties of numbers, and the search for answers continues to this day. How many primes are there? How many divisors does an integer have? Are there any other integers like $6 = 1 + 2 + 3$, where the sum of the proper divisors of the number is equal to the original number? Can one find a formula for the nth prime? Does the formula $F(n) = 2^{2^n} + 1$ yield prime values for every positive integer n? For what values of n does $2^n - 1$ give prime values? We shall consider these and other questions concerning divisibility as we develop the theory.

The first consequences of Definition 1.1, which should be reviewed at this time, are contained in the following theorems. Recall that we are using lower-case italic letters to designate integers unless expressly stated to the contrary.

Theorem 2.1.

    (i) *If $a \neq 0$, then $a \mid 0$ and $a \mid a$.*

    (ii) *$1 \mid b$ for any b.*

    (iii) *If $a \mid b$, then $a \mid bc$ for any c.*

    (iv) *If $a \mid b$ and $b \mid c$, then $a \mid c$.*

    (v) *If $a \mid b$ and $a \mid c$, then $a \mid (bx + cy)$ for any x and y.*

    PROOF. Parts (i) and (ii) are trivial since $a \cdot 0 = 0$, $a \cdot 1 = a$, and $1 \cdot b = b$.

    (iii) If $a \mid b$, there exists q such that $aq = b$. Therefore, $a(qc) = bc$ and so $a \mid bc$ for any c.

    (iv) If $a \mid b$ and $b \mid c$, there exist integers r and s such that $ar = b$ and $bs = c$. But then $c = a(rs)$ and so $a \mid c$, as claimed.

    (v) If $a \mid b$ and $a \mid c$, there exist u and v such that $au = b$ and $av = c$. Then, $bx + cy = aux + avy = a(ux + vy)$ so that $a \mid (bx + cy)$ for any x and y.

Property (v) in the preceding theorem is especially useful in solving many divisibility problems. In particular, we may note that if $a \mid b$ and $a \mid c$, then $a \mid (b + c)$ and $a \mid (b - c)$. Also, (v) could be extended to sums of more than two terms. Thus, if $a \mid b_i$ for $i = 1, \ldots, n$, then $a \mid (b_1 x_1 + \cdots + b_n x_n)$ for any integers $x_1, x_2, \ldots, x_n$.

Theorem 2.2. *If $a|b$ and $b \neq 0$, then $|a| \leq |b|$.*

PROOF. If $a|b$ and $b \neq 0$, there exists $c \neq 0$ such that $ac = b$. But then $|b| = |a| \cdot |c| \geq |a|$ since $|c| \geq 1$.

Corollary 2.3. *If a and b are positive and $a|b$ and $b|a$, then $a = b$.*

PROOF. By the preceding theorem, $|a| \leq |b|$ and $|b| \leq |a|$. But, since a and b are positive, the absolute value bars are superfluous. Thus, $a \leq b \leq a$ and so $a = b$.

In what follows, we shall have a number of occasions to use this corollary as a simple but effective tool in proving equality of numbers.

Exercises

1. If $a|b$ and $a + b = c$, prove that $a|c$.
2. If $a|c$ and $a + b = c$, prove that $a|b$.
3. If $m|(35n + 26)$, $m|(7n + 3)$, and $m > 1$, prove that $m = 11$.
4. If $m|(8n + 7)$ and $m|(6n + 5)$, prove that $m = \pm 1$.
5. If $a > 0$, $b > 0$, and $\dfrac{1}{a} + \dfrac{1}{b}$ is an integer, prove that $a = b$. Also, show that $a = 1$ or 2.
6. If $a = bq + r$ with $0 \leq r < b$ and $b|a$, prove that $r = 0$.
7. Let S be the set of all positive integers of the form $ax + by$. Suppose S is not empty and let $d = ax_0 + by_0$ be the least element in S. Show that every element of S is divisible by d. *Hint:* Let n be an element of S. Then there exist integers q and r, with $0 \leq r < d$, such that $n = qd + r$. Using the special nature of n and d, argue that $r = 0$.

2.2 The Greatest Common Divisor

If $d|a$ and $d|b$, then d is said to be a *common divisor* of a and b. If a and b are both equal to zero, it follows from (i) of Theorem 2.1 that they have infinitely many common divisors. However, if at least one of a and b is different from zero, it follows from Theorem 2.2 that the number of common divisors is finite and hence that there must be a largest common divisor.

Definition 2.1. If d is the largest common divisor of a and b, it is called the *greatest common divisor* of a and b and is denoted by (a, b).

In view of the preceding discussion, it is clear that (a, b) is defined only in case a and b are not both zero. Thus, when we subsequently have occasion to write (a, b) we shall always imply that a and b are not both zero. Also, it is clear that (a, b) is a positive integer.

If either a or b is small, the problem of finding (a, b) is not difficult since there are only a few alternatives. For example, it is easy to see that $\pm 1, \pm 2, \pm 3$, and ± 6 are the only common divisors of 12 and 18 and that $6 = (12, 18)$. However, trial and error methods are not very efficient when it comes to large values of a and b. There is an efficient and systematic way for computing (a, b), but, before discussing it, it will be convenient to present two interesting and very useful alternative characterizations of the greatest common divisor.

Theorem 2.4. *If a and b are not both zero and if $d = (a, b)$, then d is the least element in the set of all positive integers of the form $ax + by$.*

PROOF. Consider the set C of all positive integers of the form $ax + by$. By hypothesis, at least one of a and b is different from zero. For definiteness, suppose $a \neq 0$. If $a > 0$, then a itself is a member of C and if $a < 0$, $-a$ is a member of C. Therefore, C is not empty and so, by the well-ordering principle, must have a least element. Let

$$e = ax_0 + by_0$$

be the least element of C. It suffices to show that $d = e$.

By Theorem 1.7, there exist integers q and r with $0 \leq r < e$ such that $a = eq + r$. Thus,

$$r = a - eq$$
$$= a - (ax_0 + by_0)q$$
$$= a(1 - qx_0) + b(-qy_0)$$

which is of the form $ax + by$. If r were not zero, it would be a member of C, and this would contradict our assumption that e is the smallest member of C. Thus, $r = 0$ and $e \mid a$. Similarly, one can show that $e \mid b$. Thus, e is a common divisor of a and b, so that, by Definition 2.1, $e \leq d$. On the other hand, since $e = ax_0 + by_0$ and $d \mid a$ and $d \mid b$, it follows from (v) of Theorem 2.1 that $d \mid e$. Hence, $d \leq e$ by Theorem 2.2 and so $d = e$.

Theorem 2.5. $d = (a, b)$ *if and only if $d > 0, d \mid a, d \mid b$, and $f \mid d$ for every common divisor f of a and b.*

PROOF. As noted earlier, since we are discussing (a, b), we are tacitly assuming that a and b are not both zero.

(i) Suppose, first, that $d = (a, b)$. Then $d \mid a$, $d \mid b$, and by Theorem 2.4, $d = ax + by > 0$ for some integers x and y. But then, if $f \mid a$ and $f \mid b$, $f \mid d$ by (v) of Theorem 2.1.

(ii) Conversely, suppose $d > 0, d \mid a, d \mid b$, and $f \mid d$ for every common divisor f of a and b. Then d is a common divisor of a and b and, by Theorem 2.2, $|f| \leq d$. Thus, $d = (a, b)$ by Definition 2.1.

2.3 The Euclidean Algorithm

We are now in a position to discuss an orderly and systematic process for finding the greatest common divisor of two nonzero integers. Such a method is given in Book VII of Euclid's *Elements* and is now known as *Euclid's algorithm*.

For $a > b > 0$, we proceed as follows: Divide a by b getting, according to Theorem 1.7, a quotient q_1 and remainder r_1 such that $a = bq_1 + r_1$ with $0 \le r_1 < b$. If $r_1 = 0$, then $b \mid a$ and $(a, b) = b$. If $r_1 \ne 0$, we divide b by r_1 getting a quotient q_2 and remainder r_2 such that $b = q_2r_1 + r_2$ with $0 \le r_2 < r_1$. If $r_2 = 0$, the process stops. If $r_2 \ne 0$, we continue and get $r_1 = q_3r_2 + r_3$ with $0 \le r_3 < r_2$, and so on. Eventually, the process must terminate with a zero remainder since the decreasing sequence of nonnegative numbers $b > r_1 > r_2 > r_3 > \cdots$ can extend for at most b terms before reaching zero. Suppose that r_{k+1} is the first zero remainder so that we have the equations

$$a = bq_1 + r_1,$$
$$b = r_1q_2 + r_2,$$
$$r_1 = r_2q_3 + r_3,$$
$$\cdots \cdots \cdots \cdots,$$
$$r_{k-3} = r_{k-2}q_{k-1} + r_{k-1},$$
$$r_{k-2} = r_{k-1}q_k + r_k,$$
$$r_{k-1} = r_kq_{k+1}.$$

It is easy to show that r_k, the last nonzero remainder, is the desired greatest common divisor of a and b. We have that $r_k \mid r_{k-1}$ and $r_k \mid r_k$ so, using the next to the last of the preceding equations and (v) of Theorem 2.1, $r_k \mid r_{k-2}$. But then, $r_k \mid r_{k-1}$ and $r_k \mid r_{k-2}$ and so, using the third equation from the last and (v) of Theorem 2.1, $r_k \mid r_{k-3}$. This process may be continued to show that $r_k \mid a$ and $r_k \mid b$. On the other hand, if $f \mid a$ and $f \mid b$, it follows from the first of the preceding equations and (v) of Theorem 2.1 that $f \mid r_1$. But then, $f \mid b$ and $f \mid r_1$ and it follows from the second equation and (v) of Theorem 2.1 that $f \mid r_2$. Continuing this argument step by step, one finally has that $f \mid r_k$. Thus, r_k satisfies the conditions of Theorem 2.5 and so $r_k = (a, b)$, as claimed.

To make the method clear, we shall now find the greatest common divisor of 288 and 51. Performing the appropriate divisions, we obtain

$$288 = 51 \cdot 5 + 33,$$
$$51 = 33 \cdot 1 + 18,$$
$$33 = 18 \cdot 1 + 15,$$
$$18 = 15 \cdot 1 + 3,$$
$$15 = 3 \cdot 5.$$

Thus, according to the preceding discussion, $3 = (288, 51)$. Moreover, one can use the preceding equations to find x and y such that $3 = 288x + 51y$, which we know exist by Theorem 2.4. Starting with the next to the last equation and eliminating successive remainders, we obtain

$$3 = 18 - 15$$
$$= 18 - (33 - 18)$$
$$= 2 \cdot 18 - 33$$
$$= 2(51 - 33) - 33$$
$$= 2 \cdot 51 - 3 \cdot 33$$
$$= 2 \cdot 51 - 3(288 - 5 \cdot 51)$$
$$= 288(-3) + 51 \cdot 17.$$

Thus, $3 = 288x + 51y$ where $x = -3$ and $y = 17$. In passing, it may be noted that the x and y are not unique. For example,

$$3 = 288(-3) + 51 \cdot 17$$
$$= 288(-3) + 288 \cdot 51 - 288 \cdot 51 + 51 \cdot 17$$
$$= 288 \cdot 48 + 51(-271)$$

so that $x = 48$, $y = -271$ would do just as well. In fact, it is easy to see that there are infinitely many pairs of values which x and y may assume.

The point of Theorem 2.4 is not so much the fact that $d = (a, b)$ is the least positive integer of the form $ax + by$, but that d can be written in this form at all. This fact was needed in the proof of Theorem 2.5, which formed the basis for the discussion of Euclid's algorithm, and it will prove useful at other points as we continue to develop the theory. Incidentally, an expression of the form $ax + by$ is said to be a *linear combination* of a and b since each term is of *first degree* in a and b. Thus, Theorem 2.4 implies that (a, b) can be represented as a linear combination of a and b. It is important to note, however, that the converse of this statement is not true. That is, if $d = ax + by$ it does not follow that $d = (a, b)$. For, if $d = ax + by$, then $kd = a(kx) + b(ky)$ is a linear combination of a and b for every k, but not all these values can equal (a, b). From $d = ax + by$ one can conclude that $(a, b) \,|\, d$ but, without further information, this is all that can be said. On the other hand, if $1 = ax + by$, then $(a, b) \,|\, 1$ and, since (a, b) is a positive integer, it follows that $(a, b) = 1$. Thus, we have proved the following little theorem.

Theorem 2.6. $(a, b) = 1$ *if and only if there exist integers x and y such that* $1 = ax + by$.

Corollary 2.7. *If $d = (a, b)$ and A and B are defined by the equations $a = Ad$, $b = Bd$, then $(A, B) = 1$.*

   PROOF. Since $d = (a, b)$, there exist integers x and y such that $d = ax + by$. Therefore,

$$1 = \frac{a}{d}\, x + \frac{b}{d}\, y = Ax + By$$

and $(A, B) = 1$ by Theorem 2.6.

Definition 2.2. If $(a, b) = 1$, then a and b are said to be *relatively prime*. More generally, if $(a_i, a_j) = 1$ for $i \neq j$, $1 \leq i \leq r$, $1 \leq j \leq r$, the integers $a_1, a_2, \ldots, a_r$ are said to be *pairwise relatively prime*.

A great deal more can be said about the special case when two numbers are relatively prime than is contained in Theorem 2.6 and Corollary 2.7. Further results appear in the following sequence of theorems, and we shall have occasion to return to the idea again and again.

Theorem 2.8. *If $a \mid bc$ and $(a, b) = 1$, then $a \mid c$.*

PROOF. Since $(a, b) = 1$, there exist integers x and y such that $1 = ax + by$. Therefore, $c = acx + bcy$. But $a \mid bc$, by hypothesis, and so $a \mid (acx + bcy)$ by (v) of Theorem 2.1. Therefore, $a \mid c$ and the proof is complete.

Corollary 2.9. *If p is a prime and $p \mid bc$, then $p \mid b$ or $p \mid c$.*

PROOF. If $p \mid b$ there is nothing to show. If $p \nmid b$, then $(p, b) = 1$ since the only positive divisors of p are 1 and p itself. But then $p \mid c$ by Theorem 2.8.

Corollary 2.10. *If p is a prime and $p \mid a_1 a_2 \cdots a_n$, then $p \mid a_i$ for some i, $1 \leq i \leq n$.*

This corollary can easily be proved by mathematical induction and the proof is left for the reader.

Corollary 2.11. *If p, p_1, p_2, $\ldots$, p_n are primes and $p \mid p_1 p_2 \cdots p_n$, then $p = p_i$ for some i, $1 \leq i \leq n$.*

PROOF. By Corollary 2.10, $p \mid p_i$ for some i, $1 \leq i \leq n$. But $p \neq 1$ and the only positive divisors of p_i are 1 and p_i. Therefore, $p = p_i$ and the proof is complete.

Theorem 2.12. *If $(a, b_i) = 1$ for $i = 1, 2, \ldots, n$, then $(a, b_1 b_2 \cdots b_n) = 1$.*

PROOF. Suppose $(a, b_1 b_2 \cdots b_n) = d > 1$. Then, by Theorem 1.2, there exists a prime p such that $p \mid d$. Since $d \mid a$ and $d \mid b_1 b_2 \cdots b_n$, it follows from (iv) of Theorem 2.1, that $p \mid a$ and $p \mid b_1 b_2 \cdots b_n$. Therefore, by Corollary 2.10, $p \mid b_i$ for some i, $1 \leq i \leq n$. But then $p \mid a$ and $p \mid b_i$ and this contradicts $(a, b_i) = 1$ for all $i = 1, 2, \ldots, n$. Therefore, it must be the case that $d = 1$.

Theorem 2.13. *If $a \mid c$, $b \mid c$, and $(a, b) = 1$, then $ab \mid c$.*

PROOF. Since $a \mid c$ and $b \mid c$, there exist integers r and s such that $ar = c = bs$. From this it follows that $b \mid ar$. But $(a, b) = 1$ and so, by Theorem 2.8, $b \mid r$. Thus, $bt = r$ for some t and $c = ar = abt$. Therefore, $ab \mid c$ and the proof is complete.

Corollary 2.14. *If $m_1, m_2, \ldots, m_n$ are pairwise relatively prime and $m_i \mid a$ for $i = 1, 2, \ldots, n$, then $m \mid a$ where $m = m_1 m_2 \cdots m_n$.*

PROOF. The result is certainly true for $n = 1$. Suppose it is also true for $n = k$ and consider the integers $m_1, m_2, \ldots, m_{k+1}$ with $(m_i, m_j) = 1$ for $i \neq j$, $1 \leq i \leq k + 1$, $1 \leq j \leq k + 1$. By Theorem 2.12, $(m', m_{k+1}) = 1$

where $m' = m_1 m_2 \cdots m_k$ and, by the induction assumption, $m' \mid a$. But then, by Theorem 2.13, $m' m_{k+1} \mid a$ and $m' m_{k+1} = m_1 m_2 \cdots m_{k+1}$. Thus, the result is true for all $n \geq 1$, by mathematical induction.

Exercises

1. Find $(357, 629)$ and determine integers x and y such that
$$(357, 629) = 357x + 629y.$$

2. Find $(-357, 629)$ and determine integers x and y such that
$$(-357, 629) = -357x + 629y.$$

3. If a is an integer, prove that $(14a + 3, 21a + 4) = 1$.

4. If $b \neq 0$, prove that $(0, b) = |b|$.

5. Prove that $b \mid a$ if and only if $(a, b) = |b|$.

6. If $b \mid c$, prove that $(a, b) = (a + c, b)$.

7. If $(a, c) = 1$ and $b \mid c$, prove that $(a, b) = 1$.

8. If $(a, c) = 1$, prove that $(a, bc) = (a, b)$.

9. If $c > 0$, prove that $(ac, bc) = c(a, b)$.

10. If $(a, b) = 1$, prove that $(a + b, a - b) = 1$ or 2. *Hint:* Suppose that $d = (a + b, a - b)$. Show that $d \mid 2b$, $d \mid 2a$, and use the result of Exercise 9.

11. If $(a, b) = 1$, prove that $(2a + b, a + 2b) = 1$ or 3.

12. If $d \mid mn$ and $(m, n) = 1$, prove that $d = d_1 d_2$ where $d_1 \mid m$, $d_2 \mid n$, and $(d_1, d_2) = 1$. *Hint:* Let $d_1 = (d, m)$.

13. If $(a, b) = (c, d) = 1$, $b > 0$, $d > 0$, and $\dfrac{a}{b} + \dfrac{c}{d}$ is an integer, prove that $b = d$.

14. Prove that the product of any three consecutive integers is divisible by 6. *Suggestion:* Use Theorem 2.13.

15. If $(a, b) = r$, $(a, c) = s$, and $(b, c) = 1$, prove that $(a, bc) = rs$. Give an example to show that this is not true if $(b, c) > 1$.

16. For the Fibonacci sequence (see p. 10), prove that $(f_n, f_{n+1}) = 1$ for every positive integer n.

17. For the Fibonacci sequence, prove that $(f_n, f_{n+3}) = 1$ or 2 for $n \geq 1$. *Hint:* Let $d = (f_n, f_{n+3})$ and show that $d \mid 2$.

18. In the preceding exercise, $(f_n, f_{n+3}) = 2$ if and only if $2 \mid f_n$. Show that $2 \mid f_n$ if and only if $n = 3q$ for some positive integer q. *Hint:* For the "if" part, note that $2 = f_3$ and use Exercise 15, page 12. For the "only if" part, deduce from Exercise 13, page 12 that $f_n = f_{3q-1} f_r + f_{3q} f_{r+1}$ for $n = 3q + r$ and argue by contradiction, using the results of Exercises 16 and 7 above.

19. The preceding exercise can be generalized. For $m > 2$, show that $f_m \mid f_n$ if and only if $m \mid n$. *Hint:* For the "only if" part of the proof, deduce from Exercise 13, page 12 that $f_n = f_{mq-1} f_r + f_{mq} f_{r+1}$ where $n = mq + r$ and again argue by contradiction.

20. From the formula in the preceding exercise, it is easy to deduce that $(f_n, f_m) = (f_m, f_r)$ where $n = mq + r$. Using this result and the Euclidean algorithm, prove that $(f_n, f_m) = f_{(n,m)}$.

2.4 The Least Common Multiple

If $a \mid m$ and $b \mid m$, then m is called a *common multiple* of a and b. Since division by zero is meaningless, it is clear that this definition has meaning only if a and b are both different from zero. In this case it is clear that ab and $-ab$ are both common multiples of a and b and that one of them is positive. Therefore, by the well-ordering principle, there must exist a least positive common multiple.

Definition 2.3. If m is the smallest positive common multiple of a and b, it is called the *least common multiple* of a and b and is denoted by $[a, b]$.

In view of the preceding discussion, it is clear that $[a, b]$ has meaning if and only if a and b are both different from zero. Thus, in what follows, when we write $[a, b]$ we shall always understand that a and b are different from zero. The following two theorems provide alternative characterizations of the least common multiple as well as a method for computing it.

Theorem 2.15. $m = [a, b]$ *if and only if $m > 0$, $a \mid m$, $b \mid m$, and $m \mid n$ for every common multiple n of a and b.*

PROOF. Since we are discussing $[a, b]$, we tacitly assume that a and b are different from zero.

(i) Suppose, first, that $m = [a, b]$ and that n is any common multiple of a and b. By definition, $m > 0$, $a \mid m$, and $b \mid m$, and so we have only to show that $m \mid n$. There is no loss in generality in assuming that n is positive, for if n were negative we would consider $-n$. Since, by definition, m is the least positive common multiple of a and b, it follows that $m \leq n$. If $m = n$, then $m \mid n$ and we are done. If $m < n$ then, by Theorem 1.7, there exist q and r with $0 \leq r < m$ such that $n = qm + r$. Then, $r = n - qm$ and it follows from (v) of Theorem 2.1 that r is a common multiple of a and b since both m and n are common multiples of a and b. If $r \neq 0$, this violates the given condition that m is the least common multiple. Therefore, $r = 0$ and $m \mid n$ as claimed.

(ii) Suppose that $m > 0$, $a \mid m$, $b \mid m$, and that $m \mid n$ for every common multiple n of a and b. Clearly, m is a positive common multiple of a and b and so we have only to show that it is the least positive common multiple. Since $m \mid n$ where n is any common multiple, it follows from Theorem 2.2 that $m \leq |n|$. Thus, m is the least positive common multiple of a and b and the proof is complete.

Theorem 2.16. *If $ab \neq 0$, then $[a, b] = \left| \dfrac{ab}{(a, b)} \right|$.*

PROOF. Let $d = (a, b)$, $a = Ad$, $b = Bd$, and $m = |ab/d|$. Then $m = |Ab| = |aB|$ so that $m > 0$, $a \mid m$, and $b \mid m$. If $a \mid n$ and $b \mid n$, then there exist r and s such that $ar = n = bs$. Therefore, $Adr = Bds$ and $Ar = Bs$. This implies that $A \mid Bs$. But $(A, B) = 1$ by Corollary 2.7 and so, by Theorem 2.8, $A \mid s$ and there exists t such that $At = s$. But then $n = bs = Abt = \pm mt$ and so $m \mid n$. Thus, m satisfies the conditions of Theorem 2.15 and $m = [a, b]$ as we were to prove.

In view of this theorem, the computation of the least common multiple of two nonzero integers can be made to depend on the computation of their greatest common divisor which, in turn, can be computed by Euclid's algorithm. For example, since we found earlier that $(288, 51) = 3$, we now have that

$$[288, 51] = \frac{288 \cdot 51}{3} = 4896.$$

Of course, the ideas of greatest common divisor and least common multiple can be extended in a natural way to more than two numbers. Thus, if a_1, $a_2, \ldots, a_r$ are not all zero, they have a largest positive common divisor which we denote by $(a_1, a_2, \ldots, a_r)$. It can be shown that d is the g.c.d. of $a_1, a_2, \ldots, a_r$ if and only if $d > 0$, $d \mid a_i$ for $i = 1, 2, \ldots, r$, and $f \mid d$ for every common divisor f of $a_1, a_2, \ldots, a_r$. Also, it can be shown that d is the least positive integer of the form $a_1x_1 + a_2x_2 + \cdots + a_rx_r$. The integers $a_1, a_2, \ldots, a_r$ are said to be *relatively prime* in case $(a_1, a_2, \ldots, a_r) = 1$. As before,

$$(a_1, a_2, \ldots, a_r) = 1$$

if and only if there exist integers $x_1, x_2, \ldots, x_r$ such that

$$a_1x_1 + \cdots + a_rx_r = 1.$$

Similarly, if none of $a_1, a_2, \ldots, a_r$ are zero, they have a least positive common multiple which we denote by $[a_1, a_2, \ldots, a_r]$. It can be shown that $m = [a_1, a_2, \ldots, a_r]$ if and only if $m > 0$, $a_i \mid m$ for each $i = 1, 2, \ldots, r$, and $m \mid n$ for every common multiple n of the a's.

The calculation of the greatest common divisor and least common multiple of more than two integers can be accomplished in successive steps in accordance with the following theorems.

Theorem 2.17. *If none of $a_1, a_2, \ldots, a_r$ is zero, then*

$$(a_1, a_2, \ldots, a_r) = ((a_1, \ldots, a_{r-1}), a_r).$$

PROOF. Let $d = (a_1, a_2, \ldots, a_r)$ and $e = ((a_1, \ldots, a_{r-1}), a_r)$; then d and e are both positive. By Corollary 2.3, it suffices to show that $d \mid e$ and $e \mid d$. Since $d = (a_1, \ldots, a_r)$, $d \mid a_i$ for $i = 1, 2, \ldots, r$. Therefore, $d \mid (a_1, \ldots, a_{r-1})$ and $d \mid a_r$. But then $d \mid e$ by Theorem 2.5. On the other hand, $e \mid a_r$ and $e \mid (a_1, \ldots, a_{r-1})$. Therefore, $e \mid a_i$ for $1 \leq i \leq r$ and so $e \mid d$. This completes the proof.

Theorem 2.18. *If none of $a_1, a_2, \ldots, a_r$ is zero, then*

$$[a_1, a_2, \ldots, a_r] = [[a_1, \ldots, a_{r-1}], a_r].$$

The proof of this theorem, which is exactly analogous to that of Theorem 2.17, will be left to the reader.

The preceding theorems provide a systematic method for computing the greatest common divisor and least common multiple of more than two integers. For example, to find $(108, 84, 78)$ we first use the Euclidean algorithm to find that $(108, 84) = 12$ and that $(12, 78) = 6$. Hence, by Theorem 2.17, $(108, 84, 78) = 6$. Also, from the equations of the Euclidean algorithm used to compute $(108, 84) = 12$ and $(12, 78) = 6$ it is easy to find x_1, x_2, x_3 such that $6 = 108x_1 + 84x_2 + 78x_3$. These equations give $12 = 4 \cdot 84 - 3 \cdot 108$ and $6 = 78 - 6 \cdot 12$ which can be combined to give

$$6 = 78 - 6(4 \cdot 84 - 3 \cdot 108)$$
$$= 18 \cdot 108 - 24 \cdot 84 + 78.$$

Thus, we can take $x_1 = 18$, $x_2 = -24$, and $x_3 = 1$. As before, it is easy to see that x_1, x_2, and x_3 are not unique.

By Theorem 2.16,

$$[108, 84] = \frac{108 \cdot 84}{12} = 756.$$

Using the Euclidean algorithm, we find that $(756, 78) = 6$. Again, by Theorem 2.16,

$$[756, 78] = \frac{756 \cdot 78}{6} = 9828.$$

Therefore, by Theorem 2.18,

$$[108, 84, 78] = [756, 78] = 9828.$$

Exercises

1. Find $[357, 629]$.

2. Find $(357, 629, 221)$ and determine integers x, y, and z such that $(357, 629, 221) = 357x + 629y + 221z$.

3. Find $[357, 629, 221]$.

4. If $c > 0$, prove that $[ac, bc] = c[a, b]$.

5. Prove that $a \mid b$ if and only if $[a, b] = |b|$.

6. For any integer n, prove that $[9n + 8, 6n + 5] = 54n^2 + 93n + 40$.

7. Let $a_1, a_2, \ldots, a_r$ be nonzero integers. Let $d = a_1x_1 + a_2x_2 + \cdots + a_rx_r$ be the smallest positive linear combination of $a_1, a_2, \ldots, a_r$. Prove that $d = (a_1, a_2, \ldots, a_r)$.

8. Prove that $(a_1, a_2, \ldots, a_r) = 1$ if and only if there exist integers $x_1, x_2, \ldots, x_r$ such that $1 = a_1x_1 + a_2x_2 + \cdots + a_rx_r$.

9. Give an example to show that the equation

$$(a_1, a_2, \ldots, a_r)[a_1, a_2, \ldots, a_r] = a_1a_2 \cdots a_r$$

is not necessarily true.

10. Give an example to show that the equation of Exercise 9 is sometimes true. Can you discover under what conditions the equation is generally true?

2.5 The Fundamental Theorem of Arithmetic

As shown in Theorem 1.2, every positive integer greater than 1 either is a prime or can be successively factored into a product of primes. For example, $36 = 4 \cdot 9 = 2 \cdot 2 \cdot 3 \cdot 3$ where 2 and 3 are primes. Again, $36 = 6 \cdot 6 = 2 \cdot 3 \cdot 2 \cdot 3$ and we see that the same prime factors occur in each case. Indeed, it is common experience that, apart from the order in which the factors occur, factorization of an integer into a product of primes can be carried out in one and only one way. Common experience, however, is a poor substitute for proof. To illustrate this point, it is our present purpose to exhibit systems of numbers possessing many of the same properties as the set of positive integers, but where factorization into primes is not unique.

We begin by letting I denote the set of all positive integers, and considering the set T of all positive integers of the form $3k + 1$ where k is a nonnegative integer. That is, $T = \{1, 4, 7, 10, 13, 16, 19, 22, 25, 28, \ldots\}$ consists of just those positive integers which leave a remainder of 1 when divided by 3. Since

$$(3r + 1)(3s + 1) = 3(3rs + r + s) + 1,$$

it follows that the product of any two elements of T is again an element of T or, in more technical terms, that T is *closed* with respect to multiplication. Also, since T is a subset of I, certain properties of I are bound to hold in T. Thus, we need no further argument to be sure that the commutative and associative laws for multiplication hold in T and that 1 is the multiplicative identity for T, just as it is for I.

In addition to the similarities already mentioned, it is clear that T also contains prime and composite numbers, just as I does. That is, some elements in T can be factored into products of other elements in T and some cannot. For example, $16 = 4 \cdot 4$ and $28 = 4 \cdot 7$, and so 16 and 28 are composite in T. On the other hand, none of 4, 7, 10, 13, 19, 22, or 25 can be further factored in T and so are called primes in T. But the similarity between I and T ceases at this point since it is easy to see that factorization into primes in T is not unique. For example, $100 = 4 \cdot 25 = 10 \cdot 10$ and yet 4, 10, and 25 are all prime in T. Of course, none of 4, 10, and 25 are prime in the ordinary sense, but they are prime in T and so we have a legitimate example of a multiplicative system where prime factorization is not unique.

Since T and I possess precisely the same multiplicative properties, it is apparent that some other property must be basic to unique factorization. Of course, one suspects that some additive property, or at least some property involving both addition and multiplication, may be the crux of the matter, and it is certainly true that I and T differ considerably in this respect. In fact, since

$$(3r + 1) + (3s + 1) = 3(r + s) + 2,$$

it is clear that T does not contain the sum of any two of its elements and so is not even closed with respect to addition.

If we consider additive properties as well as multiplicative properties then, in addition to the laws already mentioned, it is well known that I is closed with respect to addition, that the commutative and associative laws for addition hold, and that the distributive law involving both addition and multiplication is valid in I.   However, not even all of these properties are sufficient to guarantee unique factorization as the following example shows.

We consider the set C of all complex numbers of the form $a + b\sqrt{5}i$, where a and b are integers. Typical elements of C include such numbers as $2 + 3\sqrt{5}i$, $1 - \sqrt{5}i$, $2\sqrt{5}i = 0 + 2\sqrt{5}i$, and $4 = 4 + 0\sqrt{5}i$. In particular, we note that $a = a + 0\sqrt{5}i$ so that all integers are themselves members of C.

Now, it is easy to see that the closure, commutative, and associative laws for both addition and multiplication hold in C, that the distributive law holds, and that 1 is the multiplicative identity. For example,

$$(a + b\sqrt{5}i) + (c + d\sqrt{5}i) = (a + c) + (b + d)\sqrt{5}i$$

and

$$(a + b\sqrt{5}i)(c + d\sqrt{5}i) = (ac - 5bd) + (ad + bc)\sqrt{5}i,$$

so that C is closed with respect to both addition and multiplication. The reader should check to see that the other properties hold as well.

Since we have closure under multiplication, it is obvious that C contains composite elements. Though not so easy to see, it is also true that some numbers are prime in C. Since $21 = 3 \cdot 7 = (1 + 2\sqrt{5}i)(1 - 2\sqrt{5}i)$, it will follow that prime factorization in C is not unique, provided we show that $3, 7, 1 + 2\sqrt{5}i$, and $1 - 2\sqrt{5}i$ are all prime in C.

To show that 3 is prime in C, we must show that it is impossible to find elements α and β in C, both different from ± 1, such that $3 = \alpha\beta$. This is most easily accomplished in the following way. If $\alpha = a + b\sqrt{5}i$ is any element of C, define $N(\alpha)$, called the *norm* of α, by the equation $N(\alpha) = a^2 + 5b^2$. The reader can easily show by direct calculation that, for any two numbers α and β in C, $N(\alpha\beta) = N(\alpha) \cdot N(\beta)$. Now, suppose that $\alpha = a + b\sqrt{5}i$, $\beta = c + d\sqrt{5}i$ with a, b, c, and d integers, and that $3 = \alpha\beta$. Then, $9 = N(3) = N(\alpha) \cdot N(\beta) = (a^2 + 5b^2)(c^2 + 5d^2)$. Since this is an equation in integers and $1 \cdot 9 = 9 \cdot 1 = 3 \cdot 3$ are the only possibilities for factoring 9 in positive integers, it follows that $N(\alpha) = 1$, or $N(\beta) = 1$, or $N(\alpha) = N(\beta) = 3$. In the first case, it is clear that $a = \pm 1$, $b = 0$, so that $\alpha = \pm 1$ and we have the trivial factorizations $3 = 1 \cdot 3$ or $3 = (-1)(-3)$. Similarly, $N(\beta) = 1$ implies the trivial factorization $3 = 3 \cdot 1$ or $3 = (-3)(-1)$.   Finally, $N(\alpha) = 3$ is impossible since if $|b| > 0$, then $N(\alpha) \geq 5$; if $b = 0$ and $a = \pm 1$, then $N(\alpha) = 1$; and if $b = 0$ and $|a| \geq 2$, then $N(\alpha) \geq 4$. Thus, it is impossible to find a nontrivial factorization of 3 in C and 3 is prime in C as claimed.

Similar calculations which the reader can easily perform suffice to show that $7, 1 + 2\sqrt{5}i$, and $1 - 2\sqrt{5}i$ are also prime in C. Thus, we may finally say that unique factorization does not hold in C, even though C apparently satisfies most of the same arithmetical laws as does I, where prime factorization is unique.

The preceding examples clearly demonstrate the need for giving a careful and rigorous proof of the fact that prime factorization in I is unique, even though we are quite certain, by "common experience" that this is true. There have been cases where claims supported by equally firm convictions have been proved false.

Theorem 2.19 (The Fundamental Theorem of Arithmetic). *Every integer $n \geq 2$ is either a prime or a product of primes, and the product is unique, apart from the order in which the factors appear.*

PROOF. Since the first part of the theorem is simply a restatement of Theorem 1.2, we have only to show that the representation of any integer greater than 1 as a product of primes is unique. Suppose that for some integer $a \geq 2$,

$$a = p_1 p_2 \cdots p_m = q_1 q_2 \cdots q_n,$$

where the p's and q's are primes, $m \geq 1$, and $n \geq 1$. It is no restriction to assume that $m \leq n$, that

$$p_1 \leq p_2 \leq \cdots \leq p_m \quad \text{and} \quad q_1 \leq q_2 \leq \cdots \leq q_n.$$

Since the above equality implies that $p_1 | q_1 q_2 \cdots q_n$, it follows from Corollary 2.11 that $p_1 = q_i$ for some i with $1 \leq i \leq n$. This implies that $p_1 = q_i \geq q_1$. Similarly, it can be shown that $q_1 \geq p_1$ and so, in fact, $q_1 = p_1$. Dividing these equal factors out of the initial equality, we obtain

$$p_2 p_3 \cdots p_m = q_2 q_3 \cdots q_n.$$

From this the argument can be repeated to show that $p_2 = q_2$. Similarly, it can be shown that $p_i = q_i$ for $i = 3, 4, \ldots, m$. At this stage, if m were less than n, one would have $1 = q_{m+1} q_{m+2} \cdots q_n$ which is clearly false since $q_i > 1$ for each i. Therefore, $m = n$, $p_i = q_i$ for each i, and the representation is unique as claimed.

Since the primes into which an integer can be factored need not be distinct, it follows from the Fundamental Theorem of Arithmetic that each integer $a \geq 2$ can be represented as a product $a = \prod_{i=1}^{r} p_i^{a_i}$ of prime powers. This representation is called the *canonical representation* of a. Thus, $2^2 \cdot 3$, $2^4 \cdot 3^4$, and $2^2 \cdot 5 \cdot 11$ are the canonical representations of 12, 1296, and 220 in that order. If, in a given problem, only one number is represented in this way, we usually require a_i to be positive for each i. However, for notational convenience when two or more numbers are involved, we sometimes allow some of the exponents to be zero. If $a_1 = 0$, for example, the prime p_1 simply does not occur in the canonical representation of a. This device makes it possible to write the canonical representation of any two positive integers so that they *appear* to involve the same prime factors even though they may, in fact, fail to have any nontrivial common factor. For example, we could write $12 = 2^2 \cdot 3 \cdot 5^0$ and $20 = 2^2 \cdot 3^0 \cdot 5$. And one could even write $1 = 2^0 \cdot 3^0 \cdot 5^0$. The usefulness of this device is apparent in the following important theorem.

Theorem 2.20.   Let $a = \prod_{i=1}^{r} p_i^{a_i}$ *with* $a_i > 0$ *for each* i *be the canonical representation for* a *and let* $b > 0$. *Then* $b \,|\, a$ *if and only if* $b = \prod_{i=1}^{r} p_i^{b_i}$ *with* $0 \leq b_i \leq a_i$ *for each* i.

PROOF.   If $b = \prod_{i=1}^{r} p_i^{b_i}$ with $0 \leq b_i \leq a_i$, then

$$a = \prod_{i=1}^{r} p_i^{a_i}$$

$$= \prod_{i=1}^{r} p_i^{a_i - b_i + b_i}$$

$$= \prod_{i=1}^{r} p_i^{a_i - b_i} p_i^{b_i}$$

$$= \prod_{i=1}^{r} p_i^{a_i - b_i} \cdot \prod_{i=1}^{r} p_i^{b_i}$$

$$= c \cdot b$$

where $c = \prod_{i=1}^{r} p_i^{a_i - b_i}$ and $c \geq 1$ since $a_i - b_i \geq 0$ for each i.   Therefore, $b \,|\, a$ as we wished to prove.

To prove the converse, suppose $b \,|\, a$.   Then, since there exists c such that $bc = a$, the canonical representation of a can be formed by taking the product of the canonical representations of b and c. (A canonical representation for a can be formed in this way and, since the canonical representation must be unique by Theorem 2.19, this must be *the* canonical representation.)   Thus, the primes which appear in the canonical representations of b and c must be the same as those in the canonical representation of a; i.e., $b = \prod_{i=1}^{r} p_i^{b_i}$ and $c = \prod_{i=1}^{r} p_i^{c_i}$ with $b_i \geq 0$ and $c_i \geq 0$.   Since $bc = a$, it follows that $a_i = b_i + c_i$ and so $a_i \geq b_i$.   This completes the proof.

The preceding theorem makes it extremely easy to write down all the positive divisors of a positive integer once its canonical representation has been obtained.   For example, since $72 = 2^3 \cdot 3^2$, the divisors of 72 are:

$$
\begin{array}{lll}
1 \cdot 1 & 1 \cdot 3 & 1 \cdot 3^2 \\
2 \cdot 1 & 2 \cdot 3 & 2 \cdot 3^2 \\
2^2 \cdot 1 & 2^2 \cdot 3 & 2^2 \cdot 3^2 \\
2^3 \cdot 1 & 2^3 \cdot 3 & 2^3 \cdot 3^2
\end{array}
$$

It may be noticed that there are $4 \cdot 3 = 12$ such divisors and that they are the terms in the expansion of the product $(1 + 2 + 2^2 + 2^3)(1 + 3 + 3^2)$. In fact, this product gives the *sum* of the positive divisors of 72. In general, if $a = \prod_{i=1}^{r} p_i^{a_i}$, it is clear that $\prod_{i=1}^{r} (a_i + 1)$ is the number of positive divisors of a and that the sum of these divisors is given by the product

$$\prod_{i=1}^{r} (1 + p_i + p_i^2 + \cdots + p_i^{a_i}) = \prod_{i=1}^{r} \frac{p_i^{a_i+1} - 1}{p_i - 1}.$$

It is customary to denote the number of positive divisors of a by $\tau(a)$ and their sum by $\sigma(a)$. Thus, we have obtained the following theorem.

Theorem 2.21. *If $a = \prod_{i=1}^{r} p_i^{a_i}$ with $a_i > 0$ for each i is the canonical representation of a, then*

$$\tau(a) = \prod_{i=1}^{r} (a_i + 1) \quad and \quad \sigma(a) = \prod_{i=1}^{r} \frac{p_i^{a_i+1} - 1}{p_i - 1}.$$

Also, $\tau(1) = \sigma(1) = 1$.

Canonical representations also make it very easy to find greatest common divisors and least common multiples.

Theorem 2.22. *If $a = \prod_{i=1}^{r} p_i^{a_i}$ and $b = \prod_{i=1}^{r} p_i^{b_i}$ and $a_i \geq 0$ and $b_i \geq 0$ for each i are the canonical representations of a and b, then*

$$(a, b) = \prod_{i=1}^{r} p_i^{u_i} \quad and \quad [a, b] = \prod_{i=1}^{r} p_i^{v_i},$$

where u_i is the smaller of a_i and b_i and v_i is the larger of a_i and b_i for each i.

PROOF. Let $d = \prod_{i=1}^{r} p_i^{u_i}$. Since u_i is the smaller of a_i and b_i, $u_i \leq a_i$ and $u_i \leq b_i$ for each i. Therefore, by Theorem 2.20, $d \,|\, a$ and $d \,|\, b$. Suppose $f \,|\, a$ and $f \,|\, b$. Then $|f| = \prod_{i=1}^{r} p_i^{f_i}$ with $f_i \leq a_i$ and $f_i \leq b_i$ for each i. But since u_i is the smaller of a_i and b_i, this implies that $f_i \leq u_i$ for each i. Therefore, again by Theorem 2.20, $|f| \,|\, d$ and so $f \,|\, d$. Since $d > 0$, it follows from Theorem 2.5 that $\prod_{i=1}^{r} p_i^{u_i} = d = (a, b)$ as claimed.

To complete the proof note that, by definition of u_i and v_i, $a_i + b_i - u_i = v_i$. Thus, by Theorem 2.16,

$$[a, b] = \frac{ab}{(a, b)}$$

$$= \frac{\prod_{i=1}^{r} p_i^{a_i} \cdot \prod_{i=1}^{r} p_i^{b_i}}{\prod_{i=1}^{r} p_i^{u_i}}$$

$$= \prod_{i=1}^{r} p_i^{a_i+b_i-u_i}$$

$$= \prod_{i=1}^{r} p_i^{v_i}$$

as claimed.

For example, since $1296 = 2^4 \cdot 3^4$ and $9720 = 2^3 \cdot 3^5 \cdot 5$, we immediately have that

$$(1296, 9720) = 2^3 \cdot 3^4 = 648$$

and

$$[1296, 9720] = 2^4 \cdot 3^5 \cdot 5 = 19{,}440.$$

Exercises

1. Find the canonical representation of each of the following numbers: (a) 4725 (b) 3718 (c) 3234

2. Find (4725, 3234) and (3718, 3234).

3. Find [4725, 3234] and [3718, 3234].

4. Find $\tau(4725)$ and $\sigma(4725)$.

5. Find $\tau(3718)$ and $\sigma(3718)$.

6. Find the sum of the squares of the positive divisors of 4725.

7. If $a = \prod_{i=1}^{r} p_i^{a_i}$ with $a_i > 0$ for each i is the canonical representation of a, deduce a formula for the sum of the squares of the positive divisors of a.

8. Let $a = \prod_{i=1}^{r} p_i^{a_i}$ with $a_i > 0$ for each i be the canonical representation of a. Prove that a is the square of an integer if and only if a_i is even for each i.

9. Show that the number of positive divisors of a positive integer a is odd if and only if a is the square of an integer.

10. Let $a = \prod_{i=1}^{r} p_i^{a_i}$ and $b = \prod_{i=1}^{r} p_i^{b_i}$ with $a_i \geq 0$, $b_i \geq 0$ for each i be the canonical representations for a and b. Prove that $(a, b) = 1$ if and only if $a_i b_i = 0$ for each i; i.e., if and only if a_i or b_i is zero for each i.

11. If $a = \prod_{i=1}^{r} p_i^{a_i}$, $b = \prod_{i=1}^{r} p_i^{b_i}$, $c = \prod_{i=1}^{r} p_i^{c_i}$ with $a_i \geq 0$, $b_i \geq 0$, and $c_i \geq 0$ are the canonical representations of a, b, and c, prove that $(a, b, c) = \prod_{i=1}^{r} p_i^{u_i}$ and $[a, b, c] = \prod_{i=1}^{r} p_i^{v_i}$ where u_i is the smallest of a_i, b_i, c_i and v_i is the largest of a_i, b_i, c_i for each i. This result could be extended in the same way to more than three integers.

12. State the most general conditions which assure that, for $r \geq 3$,

$$(a_1, a_2, \ldots, a_r)[a_1, a_2, \ldots, a_r] = a_1 a_2 \cdots a_r.$$

13. Let C be the set of all complex numbers of the form $a + b\sqrt{5}i$ where a and b are integers. Prove that 7, $1 + 2\sqrt{5}i$, and $1 - 2\sqrt{5}i$ are all prime in C.

2.6 Pythagorean Triplets

Everyone is familiar with the fact that the triangle with sides 3, 4, and 5 is a right triangle; or, what is the same thing, that

$$3^2 + 4^2 = 5^2.$$

Only slightly less familiar is the fact that

$$5^2 + 12^2 = 13^2 \quad \text{and} \quad 8^2 + 15^2 = 17^2.$$

The problem we wish to consider here is that of finding *all* such triplets of integers, called *Pythagorean triplets*.

In the first place, it is clear that if a, b, c is a Pythagorean triplet, then so is ka, kb, kc for any integer k. Thus, 6, 8, 10 and 9, 12, 15 are such triplets, though neither is essentially different from the parent triplet 3, 4, 5. In view of this fact, it is clear that our chore will be essentially completed if we find all Pythagorean triplets whose elements are relatively prime. Such triplets are called *primitive* Pythagorean triplets.

Suppose, now, that x, y, z is a primitive Pythagorean triplet so that $x^2 + y^2 = z^2$ and $(x, y, z) = 1$. We first show that this implies that $(x, y) = (x, z) = (y, z) = 1$. For example, if $(x, z) = d > 1$ then, by the Fundamental Theorem of Arithmetic, there exists a prime p such that $p \mid d$. Since $d \mid x$ and $d \mid z$, it follows that $p \mid x$, $p \mid z$ and $p \mid x^2$, $p \mid z^2$, and $p \mid z^2 - x^2$. But $z^2 - x^2 = y^2$. Thus, $p \mid y^2$ and, by Corollary 2.9, $p \mid y$. This contradicts $(x, y, z) = 1$; so it must be the case that $(x, z) = 1$. Similarly, one can show that $(x, y) = (y, z) = 1$.

From the preceding paragraph, it follows that x and y cannot both be even. It is also true that they cannot both be odd. This follows from the fact, discussed in Section 1.7, that the square of an odd integer must be of the form $4q + 1$ and the square of an even integer must be of the form $4q$, so that the square of an integer cannot be of the form $4q + 2$ or $4q + 3$. Thus, if x and y were both odd, then $x^2 = 4r + 1$ and $y^2 = 4s + 1$ for some r and s and $z^2 = x^2 + y^2 = 4(r + s) + 2$. This says that z^2 is of the form $4q + 2$ and this is impossible, as noted above. Hence, it must be the case that one of x and y is even, the other odd.

For definiteness, take x even and y odd. Of course, z^2 will then be of the form $4q + 1$ and so z is also odd. Hence $z - y$ and $z + y$ are both even and

$$x^2 = z^2 - y^2 = (z - y)(z + y).$$

Let $z - y = 2u$ and $z + y = 2v$. Then

$$z = v + u \qquad \text{and} \qquad y = v - u,$$

and it can be shown that one of u and v is even, the other odd, and that $(u, v) = 1$. For, if $(u, v) = d > 1$, then $d \mid u$, $d \mid v$, and so $d \mid z$ and $d \mid y$, in contradiction to the fact that $(z, y) = 1$. Moreover, if u and v are both odd, then z and y are even and this is also a contradiction.

Since x is even, $x/2$ is an integer and

$$\left(\frac{x}{2}\right)^2 = \frac{z - y}{2} \cdot \frac{z + y}{2} = u \cdot v.$$

Let $x/2 = \prod_{i=1}^{r} p_i^{a_i}$ be the canonical representation of $x/2$. Then $u \cdot v = \prod_{i=1}^{r} p_i^{2a_i}$. It follows from Theorem 2.20 that $u = \prod_{i=1}^{r} p_i^{b_i}$, $v = \prod_{i=1}^{r} p_i^{c_i}$, $b_i \geq 0$, $c_i \geq 0$, and that $b_i + c_i = 2a_i$. If b_i and c_i are both different from zero for some i, then $p_i \mid u$ and $p_i \mid v$, in contradiction to the fact that $(u, v) = 1$. Thus, one of b_i and c_i is zero for each i. It follows that b_i and c_i are even for each i, say $b_i = 2u_i$ and $c_i = 2v_i$. Then $u = s^2$, $v = t^2$ where $s = \prod_{i=1}^{r} p_i^{u_i}$ and $t = \prod_{i=1}^{r} p_i^{v_i}$. Also $(s, t) = 1$ and one of s and t is even and the other odd, since the same statements are true about u and v.

Finally, we have from above that if x, y, z is a primitive Pythagorean triplet, then there exist integers s and t, with $(s, t) = 1$ and with one of s and t even and the other odd, such that

$$\begin{aligned} x &= 2st, \\ y &= t^2 - s^2, \\ z &= t^2 + s^2. \end{aligned}$$

Moreover, it is not difficult to prove that the converse of this result is also true. In the first place, if x, y, z are defined by the preceding formulas,

$$\begin{aligned} x^2 + y^2 &= (2st)^2 + (t^2 - s^2)^2 \\ &= t^4 + 2t^2s^2 + s^4 \\ &= (t^2 + s^2)^2 \\ &= z^2. \end{aligned}$$

Also, if $(s, t) = 1$ with one of s and t even and the other odd, then x is even and y and z are both odd. Suppose that $(y, z) = d > 1$. Then there exists a prime p such that $p \mid d$. Therefore, $p \mid y$, $p \mid z$ and so p divides $z + y = 2t^2$ and $z - y = 2s^2$. But p must be odd since $p \mid z$ and z is odd. Therefore, $p \mid t^2$ and $p \mid s^2$ and so $p \mid t$ and $p \mid s$ by Corollary 2.9. This contradicts $(s, t) = 1$ and so it must be that $(y, z) = 1$. Similarly, it can be shown that $(x, y) = (x, z) = 1$. Therefore, x, y, z defined as above form a primitive Pythagorean triplet and we have proved the following theorem.

Theorem 2.23. *The integers x, y, and z with x even form a primitive Pythagorean triplet if and only if there exist integers s and t, with $(s, t) = 1$ and with one of s and t even and the other odd, such that $x = 2st$, $y = t^2 - s^2$, and $z = t^2 + s^2$.*

An interesting geometrical fact associated with Pythagorean triplets is that the inradius of the associated right triangle is always an integer. This is easily

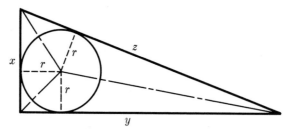

seen by computing the area of the triangle in two different ways. Suppose that x, y, z is a primitive Pythagorean triplet so that $x = 2st$, $y = t^2 - s^2$ and $z = t^2 + s^2$. Then

$$A = \frac{xy}{2} = \frac{rx}{2} + \frac{ry}{2} + \frac{rz}{2},$$

and

$$\begin{aligned} r = \frac{xy}{x + y + z} &= \frac{2st(t^2 - s^2)}{2st + (t^2 - s^2) + (t^2 + s^2)} \\ &= \frac{2st(t - s)(t + s)}{2t(s + t)} \\ &= s(t - s), \end{aligned}$$

which is an integer. If x, y, z is not a primitive triplet, then $x = k \cdot 2st$, $y = k(t^2 - s^2)$, $z = k(t^2 + s^2)$ for some k and the argument still holds.

Exercises

1. Construct a table of primitive Pythagorean triplets for the following values of (s, t): $(1, 2)$, $(1, 4)$, $(2, 3)$, $(1, 6)$, $(2, 5)$, $(3, 4)$, $(1, 8)$, $(2, 7)$, and $(4, 5)$.

2. The table of Exercise 1 suggests that one of the numbers in any primitive Pythagorean triplet is divisible by 4, one (not necessarily a different one) is divisible by 3, and one (again not necessarily different) is divisible by 5. Prove that this is so. *Hint:* By Theorem 1.7, every integer can be written in the form $3q$, $3q + 1$, or $3q + 2$. Similarly, any integer is of the form $5q$, $5q + 1$, $5q + 2$, $5q + 3$, or $5q + 4$.

3. Give values of x, y, z such that $(x, y, z) = 1$ and yet $(x, y) > 1$, $(x, z) > 1$, and $(y, z) > 1$.

4. If $x^2 + y^2 = z^2$ and $(x, y, z) = 1$, prove that $(x, y) = (y, z) = 1$.

5. If $(s, t) = 1$ and one of s and t is even, the other odd, prove that $(x, y) = (x, z) = 1$ where $x = 2st$, $y = t^2 - s^2$, and $z = t^2 + s^2$.

6. Let x, y, z be a Pythagorean triplet and consider the escribed circle as shown in the diagram:

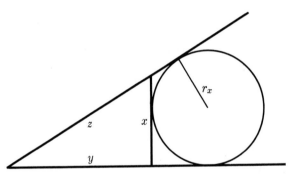

Prove that the radius r_x is an integer. *Hint:* Calculate the area of the triangle in two different ways.

7. Prove that the radii r_y and r_z of the other two escribed circles for the triangle of Exercise 6 also have integral values.

8. Prove that r, r_x, r_y, r_z of the two preceding exercises and the discussion of the text satisfy $r_z - r_y - r_x - r = 0$ and $rr_z - r_x r_y = 0$.

9. If x, y, and z form a Pythagorean triplet and r_x, r_y, r_z, and r are as in the preceding exercise, prove that $r_y r_z - rr_x = y^2$ and $r_x r_z - rr_y = x^2$. Also, prove that $r_z + r_y + r_x - r = 2z$, $r_z + r_y - r_x + r = 2y$, $r_z - r_y + r_x + r = 2x$, and that $2r_z = x + y + z$.

10. For x, y, z, r_x, r_y, r_z, and r as in Exercise 9, prove that $(r_z - r)(r_x + r_y) = z^2$.

Prime Numbers

3.1 The Sieve of Eratosthenes

The study of prime numbers naturally begins with the problem of determining whether a given integer n is prime or composite. Innocent as it may seem, this problem has no simple general solution, and we shall have to be content with partial answers. In view of the Fundamental Theorem of Arithmetic, it is clear that, in any given case, the determination could be made by successively dividing the integer in question by each of the primes which precede it, provided these primes are known. In fact, since it is evident that each composite positive integer must have a nontrivial factor not exceeding its own square root, the answer could be found for any n by successively dividing by each of the primes not exceeding $\sqrt{n}$. This greatly reduces the amount of work that must be done, but the process is still not feasible for extremely large values of n since the primes are not known much beyond 10^7.

A simple and ingenious approach to the problem which enables one to find all of the primes up to any prescribed limit is the one called the *Sieve of Eratosthenes*, after the Greek mathematician Eratosthenes (276–194 B.C.). This method consists of writing down all of the integers from 2 up to the given limit n and then sieving out, as it were, the composite numbers. We note first that 2 is the smallest prime and that the multiples of 2,

$$2 \cdot 2, \quad 2 \cdot 3, \quad 2 \cdot 4, \quad \ldots, \quad 2k, \quad \ldots,$$

occur in the list of integers at intervals of two following 2. Thus, if we strike from the list every second number after 2, we shall "sieve out" all multiples of 2 not exceeding n, and we shall retain only multiples of larger primes. Now 3, the next largest integer not struck out, is clearly a prime since it is not a multiple of the only prime smaller than itself. Again, the multiples of 3 occur in the list of integers at intervals of three following 3, so we now strike out each of these numbers not yet deleted as multiples of 2. The next number not already deleted must also be a prime, since it is not a multiple of 2 or 3, the only primes which precede it. Thus, 5 is a prime and every fifth number after 5 must be deleted as a multiple of 5. Since every composite number must have a prime factor not exceeding its own square root, every composite number in our list must have a prime factor not exceeding $\sqrt{n}$. Thus, by the time we have deleted all multiples of all primes not exceeding $\sqrt{n}$, we shall have sieved out all composite numbers and those that remain will be *all* of the primes not exceeding n.

The table which follows shows the completed sieve for $n = 200$. Note that, since $17^2 = 289$, the process is completed by the time all multiples of 13 have been struck from the list. The prime numbers have been circled to make them stand out in the table.

THE SIEVE OF ERATOSTHENES FOR $n = 200$

	2	3	4	5	6	7	8	9	10
11	12	13	14	15	16	17	18	19	20
21	22	23	24	25	26	27	28	29	30
31	32	33	34	35	36	37	38	39	40
41	42	43	44	45	46	47	48	49	50
51	52	53	54	55	56	57	58	59	60
61	62	63	64	65	66	67	68	69	70
71	72	73	74	75	76	77	78	79	80
81	82	83	84	85	86	87	88	89	90
91	92	93	94	95	96	97	98	99	100
101	102	103	104	105	106	107	108	109	110
111	112	113	114	115	116	117	118	119	120
121	122	123	124	125	126	127	128	129	130
131	132	133	134	135	136	137	138	139	140
141	142	143	144	145	146	147	148	149	150
151	152	153	154	155	156	157	158	159	160
161	162	163	164	165	166	167	168	169	170
171	172	173	174	175	176	177	178	179	180
181	182	183	184	185	186	187	188	189	190
191	192	193	194	195	196	197	198	199	200

Variations on the sieve method still provide the most effective means for computing factor tables and tables of prime numbers. Probably the best such tables (and certainly the best accessible) are those by D. N. Lehmer [Carnegie Institution of Washington, D.C., Publications No. 105 (1909) and No. 165 (1914); New York: Hafner Publishing Company, 1956], which extend to somewhat beyond ten million. Unpublished tables by J. P. Kulik (1773–1863) in possession of the Academy of Sciences of Vienna extend up to 100 million, but there is some doubt as to their accuracy.

For reference in connection with the material in this text, a table of primes less than 10,000 is given on pages 126–129.

3.2 The Infinitude of Primes

Careful study of the tables of primes suggests many interesting conjectures, some of which have been proved, while others still resist attack. For example, in the first five groups of one thousand positive integers there are, respectively,

$$168, 135, 127, 120, \text{ and } 119$$

primes. (The reader may count these in the table beginning on page 126.) However, if we skip over to the last five groups of one thousand integers preceding 10,000,000, we find that they contain

$$62, 58, 67, 64, \text{ and } 53$$

primes respectively. This suggests that the primes occur less and less frequently among the larger integers, and it also suggests that there is no end to the sequence of primes. It is, in fact, relatively easy to prove that there are infinitely many primes. Many such proofs exist, and the first proof is due to Euclid (?330–275 B.C.). It is also possible to prove that the primes occur less and less frequently among the larger integers, but the proofs are much more difficult. The first results along this line were obtained by the Russian mathematician P. L. Tchebychef in 1850. We consider Tchebychef's work in Section 3.3. The proof of the following theorem is a variant of that of Euclid.

Theorem 3.1. *There are infinitely many primes.*

PROOF. We first note that some primes do exist, so that the following argument is not vacuous.

Suppose that there are only a finite number of primes, say $p_1, p_2, \ldots, p_r$, and consider the integer $n = p_1 p_2 \cdots p_r + 1$. Clearly, $n > p_i$ for $i = 1, 2, \ldots, r$ and so n must be composite. By the Fundamental Theorem of Arithmetic, n must have prime divisors. Thus, $p_i | n$ for some i. But then $p_i | 1$, and this is impossible. Therefore, there must be infinitely many primes.

A glance at the table on page 41 shows that except for 2 and 5, all of the primes occur in the first, third, seventh, and ninth columns of the table and that there are nearly the same number of primes in each column. Larger tables show that this trend continues, so that one might reasonably guess that if the table on page 41 were extended *ad infinitum*, there would be infinitely many primes in each of these columns. More neatly put, one might guess that there are infinitely many primes of the form $10k + 1$, infinitely many of the form $10k + 3$, infinitely many of the form $10k + 7$, and infinitely many of the form $10k + 9$. Similarly, if the primes are arranged according to divisibility by 4, all except the prime 2 are of the form $4k + 1$ or $4k + 3$ and there seem to be about equally many of each type. Thus, one might reasonably guess that there are infinitely many primes of the form $4k + 1$ and infinitely many of the form $4k + 3$. The fact is that all of these guesses are correct; the results mentioned are all special cases of a most remarkable theorem proved by G. L. Dirichlet in 1837. The proof, which depends on the analytic methods of complex function theory, is much too difficult for inclusion here, so we must be content with just the statement of the theorem.

Theorem 3.2 (Dirichlet's Theorem). *If $(a, d) = 1$ with $a > 0$ and $d > 0$, then there are infinitely many primes of the form $a + kd$.*

It is clear that the conditions of Dirichlet's theorem are necessary since if $(a, d) = r > 1$, then $r \mid (a + kd)$ for every k and $a + kd$ is never a prime for $k \geq 1$. The difficulty arises in showing that the conditions are sufficient. However, certain special cases of Dirichlet's theorem can be handled by arguments similar to that of Theorem 3.1. The following theorem provides an example.

Theorem 3.3. *There are infinitely many primes of the form $4k + 3$.*

PROOF. Since 3, 7, and 11 are of this form, the following argument is not vacuous. Suppose that there are only finitely many primes of this form, say $p_1, p_2, \ldots, p_r$, and consider the number

$$m = 4p_1 p_2 \cdots p_r - 1 = 4(p_1 p_2 \cdots p_r - 1) + 3.$$

Since m is of the form $4k + 3$ and $m > p_i$ for each i, it follows that m is composite and must have prime factors of the form $4k + 1$ or $4k + 3$. Since the product of any two numbers of the form $4k + 1$ is again of that form, it follows that m has at least one prime divisor of the form $4k + 3$. Thus, $p_i \mid m$ for some i. But then $p_i \mid 1$ and this is impossible. Therefore, there must be infinitely many primes of the form $4k + 3$.

Another conjecture suggested by the tables of primes is that there are infinitely many so-called *twin primes;* i.e., pairs p and $p + 2$ which are *both* primes. The table on page 41 contains fifteen such pairs and more extensive tables show that these pairs continue to appear. There are, in fact, 36 pairs of twin primes between $10^{12} - 10^4$ and $10^{12} + 10^4$ and 1,000,000,009,649 and 1,000,000,009,651 seems to be the largest pair known. However, unlike the proof that there are infinitely many primes, the proof that there are infinitely many twin primes has not been found. A number of criteria for the existence of twin primes have been established, but the proof that they are infinite in number has resisted the efforts of the best mathematicians over the years. The most significant, though inconclusive, result was obtained in 1921 by Viggo Brun, using a variation on the method of the Sieve of Eratosthenes. Again, we must be content to state the theorem without proof.

Theorem 3.4 (Brun's Theorem). *If q runs through the series of twin primes, then $\sum \dfrac{1}{q}$ converges.*

If the preceding series were divergent, there would necessarily be infinitely many twin primes. As it is, one can only infer that the twin primes are relatively scarce and, possibly, only finite in number. This, by the way, can be contrasted with the corresponding theorem for all primes.

Theorem 3.5. *If p runs through all prime values, then $\sum \dfrac{1}{p}$ diverges.*

PROOF. Let x and j be any two positive integers, let p_i denote the ith prime, and let $N(x, j)$ denote the number of positive integers $n \leq x$ such that $p_i \nmid n$ for any $i > j$. If n is such an integer, we may write $n = rs^2$ where r and s are positive integers and where r is square-free; i.e., r is not divisible by the square of any prime. We may now estimate $N(x, j)$ by considering the number of ways of choosing r and s so as to construct n's of the desired type. In the first place, $s \leq \sqrt{n} \leq \sqrt{x}$ so that there are at most $\sqrt{x}$ possible choices for s. Also, since r is square-free,

$$r = \prod_{i=1}^{j} p_i^{\alpha_i}$$

with $\alpha_i = 0$ or 1 for each i. Since there are two choices for each α_i and j choices for i, it follows that there are precisely 2^j possible choices for r. Thus, we finally have that there exist at most $2^j \cdot \sqrt{x}$ positive integers n satisfying the given conditions so that

(1) $$N(x, j) \leq 2^j \cdot \sqrt{x}$$

for any two positive integers x and j.

Now, suppose that $\sum_{i=1}^{\infty} 1/p_i$ converges. Then, by the general theory of infinite series, there must exist some j such that

(2) $$\sum_{i=j+1}^{\infty} \frac{1}{p_i} < \frac{1}{2}.$$

For this particular value of j, we re-estimate $N(x, j)$ by estimating the number of integers $n \leq x$ which are divisible by some p_i with $i > j$ and which are, therefore, not counted by $N(x, j)$. For such an i, the integers $p_i, 2p_i, \ldots, kp_i$, where k is the largest integer such that $kp_i \leq x$, are the values of $n \leq x$ which are divisible by p_i. Thus, for each $i > j$, there are at most x/p_i such values of n. It follows that the number of values of $n \leq x$ not counted by $N(x, j)$ is at most $\sum_{i=j+1}^{\infty} x/p_i$. Thus, using (2), we obtain

(3) $$x - N(x, j) \leq \sum_{i=j+1}^{\infty} \frac{x}{p_i} < \frac{x}{2}$$

and it follows that

(4) $$\frac{x}{2} < N(x, j).$$

Combining this result with (1), we obtain

$$\frac{x}{2} < 2^j \cdot \sqrt{x} \quad \text{or} \quad x < 2^{2j+2}$$

for every positive integer x. But this is clearly false, since the set of positive integers is unbounded. Therefore, the assumption that $\sum_{i=1}^{\infty} 1/p_i$ converges is false and the proof is complete.

While it is obvious from the two preceding theorems that the set of twin primes is much less numerous than the set of all primes, the inductive evidence that there are infinitely many twin primes is quite strong. On the other hand, it is easy to show that there are arbitrarily long stretches of consecutive composite numbers; so the distribution of the primes among the integers must be extremely irregular. To see that this last assertion is true, consider the sequence $n! + 2, n! + 3, \ldots, n! + n$ for $n \geq 2$. The first of these numbers is clearly divisible by 2, the second by 3, the third by 4, and so on. Thus, we have $n - 1$ consecutive composite integers for any $n \geq 2$.

In view of this great irregularity in the occurrence of primes, it is not surprising that no general formula has been found for finding the nth prime. It has not even been possible to find simple functions which assume only prime values for integral arguments, and the only simple functions which are known to assume infinitely many prime values are the linear functions $f(n) = a + nd$ of Dirichlet's theorem. While the function

$$f(n) = n^2 - 81n + 1681 = (n - 40)^2 - (n - 40) + 41$$

yields prime values for all $n = 1, 2, \ldots, 80$, it is not presently known whether even such a simple quadratic function as $h(n) = n^2 + 1$ assumes infinitely many prime values for integral values of n. That no polynomial can assume *only* prime values is shown in the following theorem.

Theorem 3.6. *If $f(n) = a_k n^k + a_{k-1} n^{k-1} + \cdots + a_1 n + a_0$ is a nonconstant polynomial with integral coefficients, then $f(n)$ must be composite for infinitely many values of the integer n.*

PROOF. It is no restriction to assume that $a_k > 0$ so that $\lim_{n \to \infty} f(n) = \infty$. Hence, for integers m sufficiently large, the integer $f(m) > 1$. Let $y = f(m)$. Then, for any r

$$f(m + ry) = a_k(m + ry)^k + \cdots + a_1(m + ry) + a_0$$
$$= f(m) + y \cdot g(r)$$
$$= y + y \cdot g(r)$$
$$= y\{1 + g(r)\}$$

where $g(r)$ is a polynomial in r with integral coefficients whose leading term is $a_k y^{k-1} r^k$. Therefore, $\lim_{r \to \infty} g(r) = \infty$, and there must exist an integer r_0 such that $g(r) > 1$ for all $r \geq r_0$. Thus, $f(m + ry)$ is composite for all integers $r \geq r_0$ and the theorem is proved.

Exercises

1. If p is a prime different from 2 or 3, show that it must be of the form $6k + 1$ or $6k + 5$.

2. Prove that there are infinitely many primes of the form $6k - 1$.

3. Try to prove that there are infinitely many primes of the form $4k + 1$ by imitating the proof of Theorem 3.3. Why does the proof break down?

4. How many twin primes lie in the range $9000 \leq n < 10,000$?

3.3 The Prime Number Theorem

As we have seen, the distribution of the primes considered individually appears to be most erratic. Over all, however, their distribution turns out to be amazingly regular. One measure of the distribution of the primes is the function $\pi(x)$ which denotes the number of primes not exceeding x. For example, $\pi(1) = 0$, $\pi(2) = 1$, $\pi(4) = 2$, and $\pi(p_n) = n$ where p_n denotes the nth prime. An explicit formula for $\pi(n)$ for every n would be equivalent to a formula for p_n and, as mentioned earlier, no such formula is known. However, $\pi(x)$ was studied in much detail as early as the latter part of the 18th century by Legendre and also by Gauss, then still in his teens, with a view toward finding a relatively simple function whose value *approximated* that of $\pi(x)$. In particular, both men sought a function $f(x)$ such that, for large values of x, the difference between $\pi(x)$ and $f(x)$ was small in relation to $\pi(x)$. In fact, they hoped to find $f(x)$ such that

$$\lim_{x \to \infty} \frac{\pi(x) - f(x)}{\pi(x)} = \lim_{x \to \infty} \left\{ 1 - \frac{f(x)}{\pi(x)} \right\} = 0,$$

or, what amounts to the same thing, such that

$$\lim_{x \to \infty} \frac{\pi(x)}{f(x)} = 1.$$

Legendre conjectured that, for the natural logarithm,

$$\frac{x}{\log x - 1.08366}$$

was such an approximating function, and Gauss guessed that both $\dfrac{x}{\log x}$ and

$$Li(x) = \int_2^x \frac{du}{\log u}$$

were good approximating functions, with $Li(x)$ giving the better results. While neither had a proof that his function was a good approximation to $\pi(x)$ in the sense described above, it is interesting to see what actually happens for various values of x. In the accompanying table, the values in the last three columns are given to the nearest integer.

x	$\pi(x)$	$\dfrac{x}{\log x}$	$\dfrac{x}{\log x - 1.08366}$	$Li(x)$
1,000	168	145	172	178
10,000	1,229	1,086	1,231	1,246
100,000	9,592	8,686	9,588	9,630
1,000,000	78,498	72,382	78,543	78,628
10,000,000	664,579	620,419	665,138	664,918

This line of research finally culminated in the following two very remarkable theorems, which we must offer without proof. The first theorem was proved by P. L. Tchebychef in 1850, and the second, which vindicates both Legendre and Gauss, was obtained independently by J. Hadamard and Charles de la Vallée-Poussin in 1896.

Theorem 3.7 (Tchebychef's Inequality). *For all x sufficiently large,*

$$.921 \, \frac{x}{\log x} \; < \; \pi(x) \; < \; 1.106 \, \frac{x}{\log x} \, .$$

Theorem 3.8 (The Prime Number Theorem).

$$\lim_{x \to \infty} \frac{\pi(x)}{\dfrac{x}{\log x}} = 1.$$

It follows from Tchebychef's inequality that there exist positive constants a and b such that

$$a \cdot n \log n \; < \; p_n \; < \; b \cdot n \log n,$$

where p_n denotes the nth prime. This, in turn, yields an alternative proof of Theorem 3.5 since

$$\frac{1}{p_n} > \frac{1}{b \cdot n \log n}$$

and the series $\displaystyle\sum_{n=1}^{\infty} \frac{1}{n \log n}$ diverges.

Also it follows from the prime number theorem that

$$\lim_{n \to \infty} \frac{p_n}{n \log n} = 1$$

and conversely, so that this statement is equivalent to that of the prime number theorem. It may be of interest to see how the implication goes in at least one direction. Suppose we assume that

$$\lim_{x \to \infty} \frac{\pi(x)}{\dfrac{x}{\log x}} = 1.$$

Setting $x = p_n$, we have $\pi(p_n) = n$ and it follows that

(5)
$$\lim_{n \to \infty} \frac{n \log p_n}{p_n} = 1.$$

Since the logarithm is a continuous function, the logarithm of the limit of a function is the limit of the logarithm of the function, provided that the limit of the function is positive. Thus, taking the logarithm of the preceding limit, we have that

$$\lim_{n \to \infty} \{\log n + \log \log p_n - \log p_n\} = 0$$

and, hence, that

$$\lim_{n \to \infty} \log p_n \cdot \left\{ \frac{\log n}{\log p_n} + \frac{\log \log p_n}{\log p_n} - 1 \right\} = 0.$$

In order for this to be true, the limit of the quantity in braces must be zero and, since

$$\lim_{n \to \infty} \frac{\log \log p_n}{\log p_n} = 0,$$

it follows that

$$\lim_{n \to \infty} \frac{\log n}{\log p_n} = 1.$$

Using this result in (5) above, we finally obtain

$$1 = \lim_{n \to \infty} \frac{n \log p_n}{p_n}$$

$$= \lim_{n \to \infty} \frac{n \log n}{p_n} \cdot \frac{\log p_n}{\log n}$$

$$= \lim_{n \to \infty} \frac{n \log n}{p_n}$$

as claimed. The reader will find it interesting to prove the implication in the other direction.

It is also of interest to note that the prime number theorem is equivalent to the assertion that

$$\lim_{x \to \infty} \frac{\pi(x)}{Li(x)} = 1,$$

where $Li(x) = \int_2^x dt/\log t$ is the approximating function of Gauss. To see this, it is only necessary to show that

$$\lim_{x \to \infty} \frac{Li(x)}{\dfrac{x}{\log x}} = 1.$$

For, if this is so, we have

$$1 = \lim_{x \to \infty} \frac{\pi(x)}{\dfrac{x}{\log x}}$$

$$= \lim_{x \to \infty} \frac{\pi(x)}{Li(x)} \cdot \frac{Li(x)}{\dfrac{x}{\log x}}$$

$$= \lim_{x \to \infty} \frac{\pi(x)}{Li(x)} \cdot$$

Integrating by parts, we obtain

$$(6) \qquad \int_2^x \frac{dt}{\log t} = \frac{x}{\log x} - \frac{2}{\log 2} + \int_2^x \frac{dt}{\log^2 t}$$

where, as usual, $\log^2 t$ means the same as $(\log t)^2$. Since $1/\log^2 t$ is positive and decreasing for $t > 1$, it follows that, for $x \geq 4$,

$$0 < \int_2^x \frac{dt}{\log^2 t} = \int_2^{\sqrt{x}} \frac{dt}{\log^2 t} + \int_{\sqrt{x}}^x \frac{dt}{\log^2 t}$$

$$< \frac{\sqrt{x} - 2}{\log^2 2} + \frac{x - \sqrt{x}}{\frac{1}{4}\log^2 x} < \frac{\sqrt{x}}{\log^2 2} + \frac{4x}{\log^2 x}.$$

From this it follows that

$$0 < \frac{\int_2^x \frac{dt}{\log^2 t}}{\frac{x}{\log x}} < \frac{\log x}{\sqrt{x} \cdot \log^2 2} + \frac{4}{\log x}$$

so that

$$(7) \qquad \lim_{x \to \infty} \frac{\int_2^x \frac{dt}{\log^2 t}}{\frac{x}{\log x}} = 0.$$

Finally, since $\lim_{x \to \infty} x/\log x = \infty$, if we divide both sides of (6) by $x/\log x$ and make use of (7), we obtain

$$\lim_{x \to \infty} \frac{\int_2^x \frac{dt}{\log t}}{\frac{x}{\log x}} = \lim_{x \to \infty} \frac{Li(x)}{\frac{x}{\log x}} = 1$$

as claimed.

Exercises

1. Deduce from the prime number theorem that

$$\lim_{x \to \infty} \frac{\pi(x)}{\frac{x}{\log x - c}} = 1$$

for any constant c.

2. Assume that

$$\lim_{n \to \infty} \frac{n \log n}{p_n} = 1$$

where p_n denotes the nth prime and deduce the prime number theorem. *Hint:* For $x \geq 2$, determine n by $p_n \leq x < p_{n+1}$ so that

$$n = \pi(p_n) \leq \pi(x) \leq \pi(p_{n+1}) = n + 1$$

and $x \to \infty$ as $n \to \infty$.

3.4 Mersenne and Fermat Numbers

Various methods have been developed for determining whether certain special types of numbers are prime or composite, and the largest primes known have been discovered in this way. The most notable results have been achieved by Lucas, who proved in 1876 that $2^{127} - 1$ is a prime, and by D. H. Lehmer and Robinson, who used Lucas' method in combination with electronic computing machinery to prove that $2^p - 1$ is prime for $p = 521, 607, 1279, 2203$, and 2281. The last-named value of p yields a number requiring 687 digits in its decimal representation.

Primes of the form $2^p - 1$ are called Mersenne primes after the mathematician Mersenne who, in 1644, asserted the primality or nonprimality of all the numbers of this form for all prime values of p from 2 to 257. Mersenne was later found to be mistaken in the five cases corresponding to $p = 61, 67, 89, 107$, and 257, but it is interesting to note that primes of the form $a^n - 1$ must, in fact, be Mersenne primes. More accurately, we prove the following theorem.

Theorem 3.9. *If $a^n - 1$ is a prime, $n > 1$, and $a > 0$, then $a = 2$ and n is a prime.*

PROOF. Since

$$a^n - 1 = (a - 1)(a^{n-1} + a^{n-2} + \cdots + a + 1)$$

and the second factor is clearly greater than 1, it follows that $a - 1 = 1$ and $a = 2$. Otherwise, the first factor would also exceed 1 and $a^n - 1$ would be composite. Moreover, if n were composite so that $n = rs$ with $r > 1$, $s > 1$, then

$$2^{rs} - 1 = (2^r - 1)(2^{r(s-1)} + 2^{r(s-2)} + \cdots + 2^r + 1)$$

and each factor on the right clearly exceeds 1. This is again a contradiction, and so n must be a prime.

A statement similar to that of Mersenne was made by Fermat who conjectured that $2^{2^n} + 1$ is a prime for every nonnegative integer n. This is certainly true for $n = 0, 1, 2, 3, 4$. But, in 1732, Euler showed that $2^{2^5} + 1$ is divisible by 641 and so is not a prime. Subsequent investigations have proved that many other Fermat numbers are also composite, but the guess was not unreasonable, as the following theorem shows.

Theorem 3.10. *If $a^n + 1$ is a prime, $a > 1$, $n > 0$, then a is even and $n = 2^r$ for some r.*

PROOF. If a were odd, then $a^n + 1 \geq 4$ would be even and so would not be a prime. Moreover, suppose n had an odd factor greater than 1, say $n = mq$ with q odd and $q > 1$. Then,

$$a^n + 1 = a^{mq} + 1$$
$$= (a^m + 1)(a^{m(q-1)} - a^{m(q-2)} + \cdots - a^m + 1).$$

Since $q \geq 3$, both factors are greater than 1, and this contradicts the fact that $a^n + 1$ is prime. Therefore, n has no odd factor and so must be of the form $n = 2^r$ for some r.

Exercises

1. If $F(n) = 2^{2^n} + 1$ is the nth Fermat number, show that $(F(n), F(n+k)) = 1$ for every pair of positive integers n and k. *Hint:* Show that $F(n) \mid \{F(n+k) - 2\}$.

2. Deduce from Exercise 1 that there are infinitely many primes.

4

Congruences

4.1 Introduction

As we have already seen in Section 1.7, the solution of many problems in the theory of numbers depends on focusing attention on the remainders obtained when numbers are divided by other numbers. For example, when we talk about the set of even integers, we are talking about the set of numbers which leave a remainder of 0 when divided by 2. Similarly, the odd numbers are those which leave a remainder of 1 when divided by 2. From these results it follows that the square of an integer must leave a remainder of 0 or 1 when divided by 4; it cannot leave a remainder of 2 or 3. This in turn is the key to the solution of Exercise 1 in Section 1.7 where the reader was asked to show that no number in the sequence 11, 111, 1111, 11111, . . . , is a perfect square. Again, in showing that all primes other than 2 or 5 must be of the form $10k + 1$, $10k + 3$, $10k + 7$, or $10k + 9$, we are simply showing that they must leave remainders of 1, 3, 7, or 9 when divided by 10; no other remainders are possible. And another way of stating the celebrated theorem of Dirichlet (Theorem 3.2) is to say that if $0 \le a < n$ and $(a, n) = 1$, then there are infinitely many primes which leave a remainder of a when divided by n.

This idea occurred so frequently and was of such importance in number-theoretic investigations that the great Carl Gauss was led to introduce special terminology and notation to indicate when two numbers left the same remainder when divided by some number m. Gauss's idea, which is a remarkable example of the use of well chosen notation to facilitate mathematical argument, may be stated as follows: *a is congruent to b modulo m* and is written $a \equiv b \pmod{m}$ in case a and b yield the same remainder when divided by m. As we shall soon see, this notation not only provides a powerful and convenient tool for attacking many types of divisibility problems, but also suggests an extensive list of interesting investigations.

4.2 Basic Definitions and Properties

Instead of defining congruence of integers in terms of remainders as suggested above, we begin by giving the following equivalent definition.

Definition 4.1. If m is positive and $m \mid (a - b)$, we say that *a is congruent to b modulo m* and we write $a \equiv b \pmod{m}$. If a is not congruent to b modulo m, we write $a \not\equiv b \pmod{m}$.

For example, $7 \equiv 1 \pmod 3$, $6 \equiv -2 \pmod 4$, and $a \equiv 0 \pmod m$ if and only if $m \mid a$. Moreover, if a is divided by m to obtain q and r such that $a = mq + r$ with $0 \le r < m$, then $m \mid (a - r)$ and $a \equiv r \pmod m$. Thus, we have that a is congruent modulo m to its remainder when divided by m.

Throughout the remainder of this chapter, m will denote a positive integer.

Definition 4.2. If $a = mq + r$ with $0 \le r < m$, then r is called the *least residue* of a modulo m. In general, if $a \equiv b \pmod m$, then b is called a *residue* of a modulo m.

Theorem 4.1. *If a and b have the same least residue modulo m, then $a \equiv b \pmod m$, and conversely.*

PROOF. Let r and r' be the *least residues* of a and b modulo m, respectively. Then there exist q and q' such that $a = qm + r$, $b = q'm + r'$, $0 \le r < m$, and $0 \le r' < m$. By definition, $a \equiv b \pmod m$ if and only if $m \mid (a - b)$. Since

$$a - b = m(q - q') + r - r',$$

it follows that $m \mid (a - b)$ if and only if $m \mid (r - r')$. But

$$-m < -(m - 1) \le r - r' \le m - 1 < m$$

and, since zero is the only multiple of m larger than $-m$ and smaller than m, $m \mid (r - r')$ if and only if $r - r' = 0$ and $r = r'$. Thus, $a \equiv b \pmod m$ if and only if $r = r'$, as was to be proved.

The use of the symbol "$\equiv$" for congruence of integers is reminiscent of the use of the symbol "$=$" for equality. We shall soon see that the similarity is more than just notational. In fact, both relations are examples of a more general mathematical notion, that of an *equivalence relation*.

Definition 4.3. An *equivalence relation* is a binary relation E (that is, a relation involving two objects) defined for pairs of elements of a set S and having the following three properties:

   (i) aEa for any a in S.

   (ii) If a and b are in S and aEb, then bEa.

   (iii) If a, b, and c are in S with aEb and bEc, then aEc.

These three properties are called, respectively, the *reflexive*, *symmetric*, and *transitive* properties.

It is easy to see that the *equals relation* for real or complex numbers and the *congruence* and *similarity relations* for geometrical figures are examples of *equivalence relations*. On the other hand, "is a divisor of," referring to nonzero integers, is reflexive and transitive, but not symmetric and so is not an equivalence relation. Similarly, "is perpendicular to," referring to straight lines, is symmetric, but not reflexive or transitive and so also fails to be an equivalence relation.

Now, an equivalence relation E on a set S partitions S into a collection of mutually exclusive subsets in the following way. Associate with each element a of S the set S_a of all elements of S which are equivalent to a under the relation E. Since aEa for any a in S, a is in S_a for every a. Thus, each element in S is contained in at least one of the subsets just described. Moreover, if S_a and S_b are any two of these subsets, either they are identical, or they have no elements in common. To see that this is so, we note that if c is in both S_a and S_b, then aEc and cEb. But then, by the transitive property, aEb. Thus, again by transitivity, any element equivalent to a is also equivalent to b, and so S_a and S_b are identical.

The subsets of equivalent elements of the preceding paragraph are called *equivalence classes* and any element of a given class is called a *representative* of that class. For example, if we are concerned with the equivalence relation of similarity of geometrical figures, one *equivalence class* would be the set of all equilateral triangles, and any particular equilateral triangle is a *representative* of the whole class. The terminology is especially appropriate since the representative of an equivalence class truly represents every element of the class with respect to the property involved. Thus, the triangle with sides of unit length faithfully represents any equilateral triangle as far as *shape* is concerned, though it is not representative with respect to some other property, such as *area*.

In the following theorem, we show that congruence of integers is an equivalence relation.

Theorem 4.2. *Let m be a positive integer. Then the following three properties hold:*

   (i) $a \equiv a \pmod{m}$ *for any a.*

   (ii) *If $a \equiv b \pmod{m}$, then $b \equiv a \pmod{m}$.*

   (iii) *If $a \equiv b \pmod{m}$ and $b \equiv c \pmod{m}$, then $a \equiv c \pmod{m}$.*

PROOF. All three assertions follow directly from the definition of congruence. One might prove (iii) by noting that, by Theorem 4.1, a, b, and c all have the same least residue modulo m, and so $a \equiv c \pmod{m}$ as was to be proved.

The reflexive, symmetric, and transitive properties of congruences are of considerable importance and will be in constant use as our exposition proceeds. Since it is easy to overlook, the reader should note in particular that, by the reflexive property, numbers which are equal are also congruent. Thus, if $a = b$, then $a \equiv b \pmod{m}$ for any m.

Furthermore, since congruence of integers modulo m is an equivalence relation, it divides the set of all integers into mutually exclusive equivalence classes or *residue classes*, as they are called in this case. Any integer in a given residue class is congruent modulo m to any other integer in that class, and not congruent to any integer in any other class. Since, by Theorem 4.1, every integer is congruent to its least residue modulo m and the only least residues or remainders modulo m are the integers $0, 1, \ldots, m - 1$, it follows that every integer must be congruent modulo m to one of these numbers. Also, since no two of these remainders are congruent modulo m, it follows that there are precisely m residue classes modulo m, and that the integers $0, 1, \ldots, m - 1$ are representatives of these classes. If we denote by S_0 the residue class of all integers congruent to zero modulo m, then

$$S_0 = \{0, \pm m, \pm 2m, \ldots\}.$$

Similarly,

$$S_1 = \{1, 1 \pm m, 1 \pm 2m, \ldots\},$$

$$S_2 = \{2, 2 \pm m, 2 \pm 2m, \ldots\},$$

$$\cdot \cdot \cdot \cdot \cdot \cdot \cdot \cdot \cdot \cdot \cdot \cdot \cdot \cdot \cdot \cdot \cdot \cdot,$$

$$S_{m-1} = \{m - 1, m - 1 \pm m, m - 1 \pm 2m, \ldots\}.$$

Modulo 3, the three residue classes would be

$$S_0 = \{0, \pm 3, \pm 6, \ldots\}, \qquad = \{\ldots, -6, -3, 0, 3, 6, \ldots\},$$

$$S_1 = \{1, 1 \pm 3, 1 \pm 6, \ldots\} = \{\ldots, -5, -2, 1, 4, 7, \ldots\},$$

$$S_2 = \{2, 2 \pm 3, 2 \pm 6, \ldots\} = \{\ldots, -4, -1, 2, 5, 8, \ldots\},$$

and 0, 1, 2 are representative of the classes. Of course, one could choose other numbers such as 6, 4, and -4, or 0, 1, and -1 as representatives of the classes since any number in a class is a representative of that class. Somewhat differently put, it is clear from the construction of the classes that any three integers, no two of which are congruent modulo 3, constitute a complete set of representatives for the three residue classes modulo 3. Also, any m integers, no two of which are congruent modulo m, constitute a complete set of representatives for the m residue classes modulo m. In this connection, we make the following definition.

Definition 4.4. The set of integers $0, 1, 2, \ldots, m - 1$ is called the *least residue system* modulo m. Any set of m integers, no two of which are congruent modulo m, is called a *complete residue system* modulo m.

It is clear from the preceding discussion that the least residue system is a complete residue system, and that a complete residue system is simply a set containing precisely one representative of each residue class modulo m.

The importance of the preceding ideas is made clear in the following sequence of theorems, which show that in many situations, a number in a congruence modulo m may be replaced by any other representative of the same residue class modulo m without disturbing the congruence. The theorems also show that, so far as addition, subtraction, and multiplication are concerned, congruences may be treated like equalities.

Theorem 4.3. *If* $a_i \equiv b_i \ (mod \ m)$ *for* $i = 1, 2, \ldots, n,$ *then*

(i) $\displaystyle\sum_{i=1}^{n} a_i \equiv \sum_{i=1}^{n} b_i \ (mod \ m),$ *and*

(ii) $\displaystyle\prod_{i=1}^{n} a_i \equiv \prod_{i=1}^{n} b_i \ (mod \ m).$

PROOF. (i) Since $a_i \equiv b_i \ (\text{mod } m)$, there exist integers q_i such that

$$a_i - b_i = mq_i$$

for each i. Thus,

$$m \cdot \sum_{i=1}^{n} q_i = \sum_{i=1}^{n} a_i - \sum_{i=1}^{n} b_i$$

and

$$\sum_{i=1}^{n} a_i \equiv \sum_{i=1}^{n} b_i \ (\text{mod } m).$$

(ii) The second assertion is clearly true for $n = 1$. Suppose it is also true for $n = k$ and that $a_i \equiv b_i \ (\text{mod } m)$ for $i = 1, 2, \ldots, k + 1$. Then, by assumption,

$$\prod_{i=1}^{k} a_i \equiv \prod_{i=1}^{k} b_i \ (\text{mod } m)$$

and

$$\prod_{i=1}^{k} a_i - \prod_{i=1}^{k} b_i = mq$$

for some integer q. Now,

$$\prod_{i=1}^{k+1} a_i - \prod_{i=1}^{k+1} b_i = \prod_{i=1}^{k+1} a_i - b_{k+1} \cdot \prod_{i=1}^{k} a_i + b_{k+1} \cdot \prod_{i=1}^{k} a_i - \prod_{i=1}^{k+1} b_i$$

$$= (a_{k+1} - b_{k+1}) \cdot \prod_{i=1}^{k} a_i + b_{k+1} \left(\prod_{i=1}^{k} a_i - \prod_{i=1}^{k} b_i \right)$$

$$= mq_{k+1} \cdot \prod_{i=1}^{k} a_i + b_{k+1} \cdot mq$$

$$= m \left(q_{k+1} \cdot \prod_{i=1}^{k} a_i + qb_{k+1} \right)$$

so that

$$\prod_{i=1}^{k+1} a_i \equiv \prod_{i=1}^{k+1} b_i \ (\text{mod } m).$$

Therefore, by mathematical induction, the second assertion of the theorem is true.

Corollary 4.4. *If* $a \equiv b \pmod{m}$, *then*
  (i) $a + c \equiv b + c \pmod{m}$, *and*
  (ii) $ac \equiv bc \pmod{m}$ *for any integer* c.
  PROOF. Since $c \equiv c \pmod{m}$, these assertions follow directly from the two parts of Theorem 4.3 with $n = 2$, $a_1 = a$, $b_1 = b$, and $a_2 = b_2 = c$.

Corollary 4.5. *If* $a \equiv b \pmod{m}$, *then* $a^n \equiv b^n \pmod{m}$ *for any positive integer* n.
  PROOF. This follows from (ii) of Theorem 4.3 with $a_i = a$ and $b_i = b$ for each i.

As an example of the use of the preceding theorems and corollaries, suppose we endeavor to calculate the least residue modulo 7 of the quantity

$$25 \cdot 34 + 9 \cdot 8^5.$$

One approach, of course, is to perform the indicated operations, to divide the resulting number by 7, and then to see what the remainder is. However, if we note that $8 \equiv 1 \pmod{7}$, then we obtain $8^5 \equiv 1^5 \equiv 1 \pmod{7}$ by Corollary 4.5. Also, $9 \equiv 2 \pmod{7}$. Combining these last two results by (ii) of Theorem 4.3, we obtain

$$9 \cdot 8^5 \equiv 2 \pmod{7}.$$

Again, $25 \equiv -3 \pmod{7}$ and $34 \equiv -1 \pmod{7}$ so that

$$25 \cdot 34 \equiv (-3)(-1) \equiv 3 \pmod{7}.$$

Combining these results by (i) of Theorem 4.3, we finally obtain

$$25 \cdot 34 + 9 \cdot 8^5 \equiv 2 + 3 \equiv 5 \pmod{7}.$$

Thus, 5 is the desired least residue. With experience, the work can be greatly shortened by simply replacing the various numbers (other than exponents) by numbers to which they are congruent. For example, we may write

$$25 \cdot 34 + 9 \cdot 8^5 \equiv (-3)(-1) + 2 \cdot 1^5 \equiv 3 + 2 \equiv 5 \pmod{7}.$$

If the doubtful reader will do the work the hard way, he will find that

$$25 \cdot 34 + 9 \cdot 8^5 = 7 \cdot 42251 + 5.$$

We submit that the preceding approach is much easier!

As noted above, the analogy between the treatment of congruences and equalities does not extend to division. That is to say, if $ac \equiv bc \pmod{m}$, it is not necessarily the case that $a \equiv b \pmod{m}$. For example, $10 \equiv 2 \pmod{8}$ and yet $5 \not\equiv 1 \pmod{8}$. A moment's reflection will reveal why this is sometimes so. Saying that $ac \equiv bc \pmod{m}$ is the same as saying that $m \mid (ac - bc)$; i.e., that $m \mid (a - b)c$. However, this does not necessarily imply that $m \mid (a - b)$ and $a \equiv b \pmod{m}$. It could easily be the case that part of m divides c and part divides $a - b$, or even that $m \mid c$. The following theorem shows what conclusion can be drawn for the general case.

Theorem 4.6. *If $ac \equiv bc \pmod{m}$, then $a \equiv b \pmod{m/d}$, where $d = (c, m)$.*

PROOF. If $ac \equiv bc \pmod{m}$, then there exists q such that $mq = ac - bc = (a - b)c$. Dividing both sides of this equation by $d = (c, m)$, we obtain $Mq = (a - b)C$ where $c = Cd$, $m = Md$, and $(C, M) = 1$ by Corollary 2.7, page 25. Now, $M \mid C(a - b)$ and, since $(M, C) = 1$, it follows from Theorem 2.8, page 26 that $M \mid (a - b)$. Therefore, $a \equiv b \pmod{M}$. Since $M = m/d$, this completes the proof.

Corollary 4.7. *If $ac \equiv bc \pmod{m}$ and $(c, m) = 1$, then $a \equiv b \pmod{m}$.*

PROOF. This follows directly from the theorem since $d = 1$.

Exercises

1. Which of the following are equivalence relations? If a relation is not an equivalence relation, explain why.
   (a) The relation of parallelism for lines.
   (b) The relation of "less than or equals" for real numbers.
   (c) The inclusion relation for sets.
   (d) The equality relation for sets.

2. Give an example of a relation defined on a set and having the following properties:
   (a) The relation is reflexive and symmetric, but not transitive.
   (b) The relation is transitive, but not reflexive or symmetric.

3. Find the least residue modulo 7 of the quantity $22 \cdot 51 + 698$.

4. Find the least residue modulo 5 of 3^2 and 3^{20}.

5. Find the least residue modulo 7 of 10^{515}.

6. Prove that the thirty-seventh Mersenne number, $2^{37} - 1$, is divisible by 223; i.e., that $2^{37} \equiv 1 \pmod{223}$.

7. Show that the numbers $-13, -9, -4, -1, 9, 18, 21$ form a complete residue system modulo 7.

8. Show that any m consecutive integers form a complete residue system modulo m.

9. If $a_1, a_2, \ldots, a_m$ form a complete residue system modulo m and $(k, m) = 1$, prove that $ka_1, ka_2, \ldots, ka_m$ also form a complete residue system modulo m.

10. Find a complete residue system modulo 5 composed entirely of multiples of 9.

11. Show that $1^2, 2^2, \ldots, m^2$ is not a complete residue system modulo m if $m > 2$.

12. Prove that a perfect square must have one of 0, 1, 4, 5, 6, or 9 for its units digit and that a perfect fourth power must have 0, 1, 5, or 6 for its units digit. *Hint:* An integer is congruent modulo 10 to its units digit.

13. Show that any one of the ten digits can occur as the units digit of the cube of an integer.

14. Prove that 17 does not divide $5n^2 + 15$ for any integer n.

15. If $a \equiv b \pmod{m}$ and $n \mid m$, prove that $a \equiv b \pmod{n}$.

16. If n is an integer not divisible by 2 or 3, show that $n^2 \equiv 1 \pmod{24}$.

17. If a is a positive odd integer, prove that $a^{2^n} \equiv 1 \pmod{2^{n+2}}$ for every positive integer n.

18. Compute the least residues modulo 7 of $f(2)$, $f(-5)$, $f(16)$, $f(-12)$, and $f(9)$ if $f(x) = 23x^4 - 9x^3 + 5$.

19. Compute the least residues modulo 12 of $f(-4)$, $f(8)$, $f(20)$, and $f(32)$ if $f(x) = 11x^4 - 7x^2 + 23x + 7$.

20. Carefully examine the results of Exercises 18 and 19 and see if you can guess a general rule.

21. Determine the least residue of $(n - 1)!$ modulo n for several values of n and see if you can guess a general rule.

22. If $a \equiv b \pmod{m}$, $a \equiv b \pmod{n}$, and $(m, n) = 1$, prove that $a \equiv b \pmod{mn}$. *Hint:* Use Theorem 2.13.

23. If $a \equiv b \pmod{m_i}$ for $i = 1, 2, \ldots, r$ and $(m_i, m_j) = 1$ for $i \neq j$, prove that $a \equiv b \pmod{m}$ where $m = \prod_{i=1}^{r} m_i$.

24. Prove that $a^3 \equiv a \pmod 3$ and $a^5 \equiv a \pmod 5$ for every integer a.

25. Prove that $a^5 \equiv a \pmod{15}$ for every integer a.

26. Prove that $a^{21} \equiv a \pmod{15}$ for every integer a.

27. If p is a prime and $a^2 \equiv 1 \pmod p$, prove that $a \equiv \pm 1 \pmod p$.

28. Give an example to show that the result of Exercise 27 is not valid if p is not a prime.

4.3 Special Divisibility Criteria

Everyone knows that an integer is divisible by 2 if and only if the last digit in its decimal representation is even. This is so since any integer n can be represented in the form $n = 10k + u$, where u is the last digit in the decimal representation of n. Clearly, $2 \mid n$ if and only if $2 \mid u$. Similarly, an integer is divisible by 5 if and only if the last digit in its decimal representation is 0 or 5. Simple criteria for divisibility by 3, 9, and 11 also exist and can easily be deduced from the theorems in the preceding section. We shall first prove a general theorem having to do with congruences involving polynomials with integral coefficients.

Theorem 4.8. *Let* $f(x) = \sum_{k=0}^{n} c_k x^k$ *where* $c_0, c_1, \ldots, c_n$ *are integers. If* $a \equiv b \pmod m$, *then* $f(a) \equiv f(b) \pmod m$.

PROOF. By Corollary 4.5, $a^k \equiv b^k \pmod m$ for $k = 0, 1, \ldots, n$. Therefore, by Corollary 4.4,

$$c_k a^k \equiv c_k b^k \pmod m$$

for each k. Thus, using (i) of Theorem 4.3, we obtain

$$\sum_{k=0}^{n} c_k a^k \equiv \sum_{k=0}^{n} c_k b^k \pmod m$$

so that $f(a) \equiv f(b) \pmod m$ and the proof is complete.

Theorem 4.9.   *Let* $a = \sum_{k=0}^{n} a_k 10^k$ *be the decimal representation of* a, *let* $s = \sum_{k=0}^{n} a_k$, *and let* $t = \sum_{k=0}^{n} (-1)^k a_k$. *Then*

(i) $9 \mid a$ *if and only if* $9 \mid s$;

(ii) $3 \mid a$ *if and only if* $3 \mid s$;

(iii) $11 \mid a$ *if and only if* $11 \mid t$.

PROOF.   (i) It is clear that $a = f(10)$ where $f(x) = \sum_{k=0}^{n} a_k x^k$ and that $s = f(1)$.   Since $10 \equiv 1 \pmod 9$, it follows from Theorem 4.8 that $a \equiv s \pmod 9$. Therefore, $a - s = 9q$ for some q and from this it follows that $9 \mid a$ if and only if $9 \mid s$.

(ii) and (iii) The proof for 3 is exactly the same as for 9. The proof for 11 follows from the fact that $10 \equiv -1 \pmod{11}$ and that $t = f(-1)$.

As examples of the preceding theorem, we note that 340,722 is divisible by 9, since 9 divides $3 + 4 + 0 + 7 + 2 + 2$, that 41,811 is divisible by 3, since 3 divides $4 + 1 + 8 + 1 + 1$, and that 304,161 is divisible by 11, since 11 divides $-3 + 0 - 4 + 1 - 6 + 1$. On the other hand, 357,266 is not divisible by 3, 9, or 11, since $3 + 5 + 7 + 2 + 6 + 6$ is not divisible by 3 or 9 and $-3 + 5 - 7 + 2 - 6 + 6$ is not divisible by 11.

Exercises

1. Check the following numbers for divisibility by 3, 9, and 11: (a) 37,686 (b) 113,058   (c) 20,004   (d) 371,684.

2. Note that $10^3 \equiv -1 \pmod 7$ and develop a criterion for divisibility by 7.

3. Develop a criterion for divisibility by 13.

4. Let $a = a_k b^k + a_{k-1} b^{k-1} + \cdots + a_1 b + a_0$ be the positional representation of a to base b where $b > 1$. Develop criteria for divisibility of a by divisors of $b - 1$ and $b + 1$.

5. A common error in banking is to make an interchange or transposition of some of the digits involved in an amount. For example, a teller may pay $43.34 on a check actually written for $34.43 and so be short $8.91 at the end of the day. Prove that any such error always leads to an outage, in pennies, which is divisible by 9.

4.4 Reduced Residue Systems and the Euler ϕ-Function

Many times in the theory of congruences, numbers which are relatively prime to the modulus play a unique role. Thus, as we have seen, if $ac \equiv bc \pmod m$ and $(c, m) = 1$, then $a \equiv b \pmod m$. Again, if $a_1, a_2, \ldots, a_m$ form a complete residue system modulo m and $(k, m) = 1$, then $ka_1, ka_2, \ldots, ka_m$ also form a complete residue system modulo m. Similar situations occur frequently, and so it is worthwhile to give special attention to numbers which have this property.

First of all, we note that if a and m are relatively prime, then all of the integers in the residue class S_a are also relatively prime to m. In fact, as the following theorem shows, if $(a, m) = d$, then $(b, m) = d$ for any b in the residue class S_a.

Theorem 4.10. *If $a \equiv b \pmod{m}$, then $(a, m) = (b, m)$.*

PROOF. Since $a \equiv b \pmod{m}$, there exists q such that $a - b = mq$. From this it follows that any common divisor of a and m is also a common divisor of b and m, and conversely. Therefore, since any common divisor of two integers divides their greatest common divisor, $(a, m) \mid (b, m)$ and $(b, m) \mid (a, m)$. Finally, since both of these quantities are positive, they are equal by Corollary 2.3.

Since all of the elements in S_a are relatively prime to m if a is relatively prime to m, it follows that any two complete residue systems contain the same number of integers which are relatively prime to m and that these integers are congruent modulo m in pairs. For example, in the complete residue systems $\{1, 2, 3, 4, 5, 6, 7, 8\}$ and $\{9, 10, -5, -4, 21, -10, 7, 16\}$ modulo 8, the integers 1, 3, 5, 7 and 9, -5, 21, 7 are relatively prime to 8, and $1 \equiv 9$, $3 \equiv -5$, $5 \equiv 21$, and $7 \equiv 7$, all modulo 8. More generally, to find which integers are relatively prime to m, it is only necessary to determine which of the integers $1, 2, \ldots, m$ have this property. Any other integer which is relatively prime to m must then be congruent to one of those selected from this set. These considerations are formalized in the following definitions.

Definition 4.5. The number of positive integers not exceeding m which are relatively prime to m is designated by the function $\phi(m)$. $\phi(m)$ is called the *Euler ϕ-function* after its originator, Leonard Euler (1707–1783).

Definition 4.6. Any set of $\phi(m)$ integers which are relatively prime to m and which are mutually incongruent modulo m is called a *reduced residue system* modulo m.

According to these definitions, $\phi(8) = 4$, and $\{1, 3, 5, 7\}$ and $\{9, -5, 21, 7\}$ are reduced residue systems modulo 8. Also, $\phi(1) = 1$, $\phi(2) = 1$, $\phi(6) = 2$, and $\phi(7) = 6$. Since all the positive integers not exceeding p are relatively prime to p if p is a prime, we further have that $\phi(p) = p - 1$ and that the numbers $1, 2, \ldots, p - 1$ form a reduced residue system modulo p. Finally, if $n = \prod_{i=1}^{r} p_i^{\alpha_i}$ with $\alpha_i \geq 1$ for each i is the canonical representation of n, it can be shown that

$$\phi(n) = \prod_{i=1}^{r} p_i^{\alpha_i - 1}(p_i - 1).$$

The proof of this fact is not too difficult, but we prefer to defer it until the more general discussion of Chapter 6.

Theorem 4.11. *If $a_1, a_2, \ldots, a_{\phi(m)}$ form a reduced residue system modulo m and $(k, m) = 1$, then $ka_1, ka_2, \ldots, ka_{\phi(m)}$ also form a reduced residue system modulo m.*

PROOF. Since we have the correct number of elements in the set $ka_1, \ldots, ka_{\phi(m)}$, it is only necessary to show that each of the numbers in the set is relatively prime to m and that no two are congruent modulo m. Of course, since $a_1, a_2, \ldots, a_{\phi(m)}$ form a reduced residue system modulo m, we have that $(a_i, m) = 1$ for each i and that $a_i \not\equiv a_j \pmod{m}$ if $i \neq j$.

(i) Since $(a_i, m) = 1$ for each i and $(k, m) = 1$, it follows directly from Theorem 2.12, page 26 that $(ka_i, m) = 1$ for each i.

(ii) Suppose $ka_i \equiv ka_j \pmod{m}$ with $i \neq j$. Since $(k, m) = 1$, it follows from Corollary 4.7 that $a_i \equiv a_j \pmod{m}$. But this is a contradiction, and so $ka_i \not\equiv ka_j \pmod{m}$ for $i \neq j$ and the proof is complete.

Theorem 4.12 (Fermat's Theorem). *If p is a prime and $p \nmid a$, then*

$$a^{p-1} \equiv 1 \pmod{p}.$$

PROOF. Since $\phi(p) = p - 1$, this theorem is a direct corollary of the following more general result of Euler.

Theorem 4.13 (The Euler-Fermat Theorem). *If $(a, m) = 1$, then*

$$\cdot a^{\phi(m)} \equiv 1 \pmod{m}.$$

PROOF. Let $a_1, a_2, \ldots, a_{\phi(m)}$ constitute a reduced residue system modulo m. Since $(a, m) = 1$, it follows from Theorem 4.11 that $aa_1, aa_2, \ldots, aa_{\phi(m)}$ also form a reduced residue system modulo m. Hence to each i with $1 \leq i \leq \phi(m)$, there corresponds precisely one j with $1 \leq j \leq \phi(m)$ such that

$$aa_i \equiv a_j \pmod{m}.$$

Taking the product of these $\phi(m)$ congruences and noting that

$$\prod_{i=1}^{\phi(m)} a_i = \prod_{j=1}^{\phi(m)} a_j,$$

we obtain

$$a^{\phi(m)} \cdot \prod_{i=1}^{\phi(m)} a_i \equiv \prod_{i=1}^{\phi(m)} a_i \pmod{m}.$$

Since $(a_i, m) = 1$ for each i, it follows from Theorem 2.12 that

$$\left(\prod_{i=1}^{\phi(m)} a_i, m \right) = 1.$$

Therefore, by Corollary 4.7, we may divide both sides of the preceding congruence by $\prod_{i=1}^{\phi(m)} a_i$ to obtain

$$a^{\phi(m)} \equiv 1 \pmod{m}$$

as desired.

It is easy to see that Fermat's theorem can be stated in a slightly more general way which removes the restriction that $p \nmid a$.

Corollary 4.14 (Alternative Statement of Fermat's Theorem). *If p is a prime, then $a^p \equiv a$ (mod p) for any a.*

PROOF. If $p \nmid a$, then $a^{p-1} \equiv 1$ (mod p). Therefore, multiplying both sides of the congruence by a according to Corollary 4.4, we obtain $a^p \equiv a$ (mod p).

If $p \mid a$, then $a \equiv 0$ (mod p) and $a^p \equiv 0$ (mod p), by Corollary 4.5. Therefore, by transitivity, $a^p \equiv a$ (mod p) in this case as well.

It is reasonable to expect that the Euler-Fermat theorem might be generalized along the same lines as the preceding generalization of Fermat's theorem. A natural guess would be that

$$a^m \equiv a^{m-\phi(m)} \pmod{m}$$

for any a since, for $m = p$, this reduces to the statement of Corollary 4.14. It turns out that this guess is correct, but we shall not give the proof here.

Exercises

1. Show that the numbers -30, -19, -15, -4, 15, and 39 form a reduced residue system modulo 7.

2. Find a reduced residue system modulo 7 composed entirely of multiples of 3.

3. Let $S = \{a_1, a_2, \ldots, a_{\phi(m)}\}$ with $a_i < a_{i+1}$ for all i be the reduced residue system chosen from among the least residue system modulo m, so that $0 < a_i < m$ and $(a_i, m) = 1$ for each i. Show that $m - a_i = a_{\phi(m)-i+1}$ for each i so that $S = T$ where $T = \{m - a_1, m - a_2, \ldots, m - a_{\phi(m)}\}$.

4. Show that the numbers 3, 3^2, 3^3, 3^4, 3^5, 3^6 form a reduced residue system modulo 7.

5. If p is a prime and $p \nmid a$, then $a^{p-1} \equiv 1$ (mod p) by Fermat's theorem. If $p - 1$ is the smallest positive value of e such that $a^e \equiv 1$ (mod p), prove that $a, a^2, \ldots, a^{p-1}$ form a reduced residue system modulo p.

6. State and prove a generalization of Exercise 5 valid for any positive integer m.

7. Show that 5, 5^2, 5^3, 5^4, 5^5, 5^6 form a reduced residue system modulo 18.

8. If $\alpha \geq 1$ is an integer, prove that $\phi(p^\alpha) = p^{\alpha-1}(p - 1)$.

9. Show that $\phi(16) \cdot \phi(9) = \phi(16 \cdot 9)$.

10. Prove that $a^{13} \equiv a$ (mod 2730) for any integer a.

11. If p and q are distinct primes, prove that $p^{q-1} + q^{p-1} \equiv 1$ (mod pq).

12. If p and q are distinct primes, prove that $p^q + q^p \equiv p + q$ (mod pq).

13. If p is a prime other than 2 or 5, prove that p divides infinitely many of the numbers $9, 99, 999, 9999, \ldots$.

14. If p is a prime and $1 \leq k \leq p - 1$, prove that $\binom{p}{k} = \dfrac{p!}{k!(p - k)!} \equiv 0$ (mod p).

15. Use the result of Exercise 14 to show that $(a + b)^p \equiv a^p + b^p$ (mod p) for any prime p.

16. Use the result of Exercise 15 and mathematical induction to give an alternative proof of Fermat's theorem.

17. Deduce the result of Exercise 15 from Fermat's theorem.

18. If p is a prime and $a^p \equiv b^p$ (mod p), prove that $a^p \equiv b^p$ (mod p^2). *Hint:* Deduce from Fermat's theorem that $a \equiv b$ (mod p).

5

Conditional Congruences

5.1 Introduction

If $f(a) = 0$, a is said to be a solution of the conditional equation $f(x) = 0$. Similarly, if $f(a) \equiv 0 \pmod{m}$, a is said to be a solution of the *conditional congruence* $f(x) \equiv 0 \pmod{m}$. In this chapter, we consider the problem of finding integral solutions of conditional congruences where $f(x)$ is a polynomial with integral coefficients.

Since, by Theorem 4.8, $f(a) \equiv f(b) \pmod{m}$ if $a \equiv b \pmod{m}$, it is clear that all of the solutions will be known provided we find all of the solutions in any complete residue system modulo m. Thus, unless there is a special reason for doing otherwise, we shall list only those solutions in the least residue system $0, 1, \ldots, m - 1$. Also, if we say that a congruence has r solutions or r incongruent solutions, we shall mean that precisely r of the numbers in any complete residue system modulo m are solutions of the congruence.

5.2 Linear Congruences

As with equations, the conditional congruence $f(x) \equiv 0 \pmod{m}$ is said to be *linear* in the case where $f(x)$ is a polynomial of first degree. Conditions for the solvability of such congruences are easily given.

Theorem 5.1. *The linear congruence $ax \equiv b \pmod{m}$ is solvable if and only if $d \mid b$ where $d = (a, m)$. If there are any solutions, then there are precisely d incongruent solutions.*

PROOF. Suppose that $d \mid b$, then $kd = b$ for some integer k. Since $d = (a, m)$, it follows from Theorem 2.4, page 23, that there exist integers r and s such that $d = ar + ms$. Multiplying by k, we obtain $b = kd = akr + mks$. Therefore, $akr \equiv b \pmod{m}$ and kr is a solution of the given congruence.

Conversely, suppose that x_0 is a solution of the given congruence. Then $ax_0 \equiv b \pmod{m}$ and there exists an integer q such that $ax_0 - b = qm$. Since $d \mid a$ and $d \mid m$, this implies that $d \mid b$ as claimed.

Finally, if x_0 is a solution of the given congruence,

$$a\left(x_0 + \frac{km}{d}\right) = ax_0 + km \cdot \frac{a}{d} \equiv ax_0 \equiv b \pmod{m}$$

since $d \mid a$. Thus,

$$x_0 + \frac{km}{d}$$

is a solution of the given congruence for every integer k. Moreover, if x_0 and x_1 are both solutions of the congruence, then

$$ax_1 \equiv b \equiv ax_0 \pmod{m}.$$

Therefore, by Theorem 4.6, page 58,

$$x_1 \equiv x_0 \pmod{m/d}$$

and there must exist an integer k such that

$$x_1 = x_0 + \frac{km}{d}.$$

Thus, it follows that if x_0 is a solution of the given congruence, then $x_0 + km/d$ is a solution for every k and that every solution is of this form.

In view of the preceding paragraph, the series

$$\ldots,\ x_0 - \frac{m}{d},\ x_0,\ x_0 + \frac{m}{d},\ x_0 + \frac{2m}{d},\ \ldots,\ x_0 + \frac{(d-1)m}{d},\ x_0 + \frac{dm}{d},\ \ldots$$

contains *all* solutions of the given congruence. How many are incongruent modulo m? It is clear that the d solutions

$$x_0,\ x_0 + \frac{m}{d},\ \ldots,\ x_0 + \frac{(d-1)m}{d}$$

are incongruent, since no two of these can differ by a multiple of m. Moreover, for any k, $x_0 + km/d$ is congruent to one of these d solutions modulo m. To see this, note that for any k there exist q and r with $0 \le r < d$ such that $k = qd + r$. Therefore,

$$x_0 + \frac{km}{d} = x_0 + \frac{(qd+r)m}{d}$$
$$= x_0 + qm + \frac{rm}{d}$$
$$\equiv x_0 + \frac{rm}{d} \pmod{m}$$

and $x_0 + rm/d$ is one of the above list of d solutions.

EXAMPLE 5.1. Solve $51x \equiv 21 \pmod{36}$.

Solution. In the first place, since $51 \equiv 15 \pmod{36}$, $51x \equiv 15x \pmod{36}$ for any x and the given congruence can be replaced by

$$15x \equiv 21 \pmod{36}.$$

Since $(15, 36) = 3$, there must be three incongruent solutions. Indeed, since -1 is obviously a solution and $m/d = 12$, it follows from the preceding theorem that any number which differs from -1 by a multiple of 12 is also a solution. Thus, the three solutions in the least residue system $0, 1, \ldots, 35$ are 11, 23, and 35.

If it is not possible to guess a solution to a linear congruence, one can use the Euclidean algorithm and the construction of the preceding proof to obtain the desired result. For the present example, one obtains $3 = 5 \cdot 15 - 2 \cdot 36$ so that $21 = 35 \cdot 15 - 14 \cdot 36$. Converting this to a congruence, we obtain $35 \cdot 15 \equiv 21 \pmod{36}$ so that 35 is a solution of the given congruence. The other solutions are now found as before.

Another possibility for finding the solution of the given congruence is to reduce $15x \equiv 21 \pmod{36}$ to $5x \equiv 7 \pmod{12}$ by Theorem 4.6, page 58. With the congruence in this form, it is not difficult to find a number whose product with 5 is congruent to 1 modulo 12. In this case, 5 is the desired number and multiplication of both sides of the congruence by 5 yields $25x \equiv 35 \pmod{12}$. But $25 \equiv 1 \pmod{12}$ and $35 \equiv 11 \pmod{12}$, so that this is equivalent to $x \equiv 11 \pmod{12}$. Since this argument is reversible, $x = 11$ is a solution of the given congruence and the other solutions may be found from this one, as before.

EXAMPLE 5.2. Solve $22x \equiv 4 \pmod{30}$.

Solution. A brief solution of this congruence might look as follows:

$$22x \equiv 4 \pmod{30},$$
$$11x \equiv 2 \pmod{15},$$
$$-4x \equiv 2 \pmod{15},$$
$$-16x \equiv 8 \pmod{15},$$
$$-x \equiv 8 \pmod{15},$$
$$x \equiv -8 \pmod{15}.$$

Therefore, the two solutions in the least residue system $0, 1, \ldots, 29$ are $-8 + 15 = 7$ and $-8 + 30 = 22$.

The preceding methods make it possible to solve a host of interesting problems in a systematic and efficient way. For example, consider the following problem, proposed by Euler. "Divide 100 into two positive summands one of which is divisible by 7 and the other by 11." Obviously, the problem reduces to that of finding positive integral values for x and y which satisfy the equation

$$7x + 11y = 100.$$

It is clear that integral values x_0, y_0 satisfying this equation exist if and only if $7x_0 \equiv 100 \pmod{11}$ and $11y_0 \equiv 100 \pmod{7}$. Thus, the solution of the equation $7x + 11y = 100$ in integers is equivalent to the solution of either of the congruences $7x \equiv 100 \pmod{11}$ or $11y \equiv 100 \pmod{7}$. Working with the latter congruence because of its smaller modulus, we obtain

$$4y \equiv 2 \pmod{7},$$
$$8y \equiv 4 \pmod{7},$$
$$y \equiv 4 \pmod{7}.$$

Thus, possible positive values of y which satisfy the original equation are $4, 11, 18, \ldots$. Computing the corresponding values of x from the original equation, we obtain $8, -3, -14, \ldots$. Thus, the only solution in positive integers is $x = 8$, $y = 4$ and the desired summands are 56 and 44.

In general, an equation to be solved in integers is called a *Diophantine equation* after the Greek mathematician Diophantus of Alexandria, who lived about A.D. 250. The preceding argument, which is essentially general, shows that the solution of the linear Diophantine equation

$$ax + by = r$$

is equivalent to the solution of either of the congruences

$$ax \equiv r \pmod{b} \quad \text{or} \quad by \equiv r \pmod{a}.$$

By Theorem 5.1, we know that solution is possible if and only if $d \mid r$ where $d = (a, b)$. Also, if x_0 is any solution of $ax \equiv r \pmod{b}$, then every solution is given by

$$x_k = x_0 + \frac{kb}{d}.$$

Moreover, the y value corresponding to each x value can be computed from $ax + by = r$. Therefore,

$$y_0 = \frac{r - ax_0}{b}$$

and, for each k,

$$y_k = \frac{r - ax_k}{b}$$
$$= \frac{r - a(x_0 + kb/d)}{b}$$
$$= \frac{r - ax_0}{b} - \frac{ka}{d}$$
$$= y_0 - \frac{ka}{d}.$$

Thus, we have proved the following theorem.

Theorem 5.2. *The linear Diophantine equation $ax + by = r$ is solvable (in integers) if and only if $d \mid r$ where $d = (a, b)$. If x_0, y_0 is any solution, then every solution is given by*

$$x_k = x_0 + \frac{kb}{d}, \qquad y_k = y_0 - \frac{ka}{d},$$

where $k = 0, \pm 1, \pm 2, \ldots$.

Exercises

1. Solve the following conditional congruences:
   (a) $25x \equiv 4 \pmod{11}$ (b) $15x \equiv 3 \pmod{9}$
   (c) $34x \equiv 60 \pmod{98}$ (d) $35x \equiv 15 \pmod{182}$
2. Find all integral solutions of the equation $15x + 7y = 110$.

3. A farmer buys 100 birds for $100. If chicks cost 50 cents each, ducks $3 each, turkeys $10 each, and the farmer obtained at least one bird of each type, how many of each type did he buy?

4. When a man cashed a check, the clerk mistook the number of cents for the number of dollars and vice versa. After spending 68 cents, the man discovered that he still had precisely twice as much money as the amount for which the check was originally written. What is the smallest amount for which the check could have been written?

5. Find all solutions, in integers, of $17x - 11y = 272$.

6. Prove that $ax + by + cz = r$ is solvable in integers if and only if $d \mid r$, where $d = (a, b, c)$.

7. Find a solution in integers of $48x + 17y - 66z = 9$.

8. If $(a, m) = 1$, then $a^{\phi(m)} \equiv 1 \pmod{m}$ by the Euler-Fermat theorem. Therefore, to solve $ax \equiv b \pmod{m}$, one can multiply both sides of the congruence by $a^{\phi(m)-1}$, obtaining

$$x \equiv a^{\phi(m)}x \equiv ba^{\phi(m)-1} \pmod{m}.$$

Use this method to solve $77x \equiv 28 \pmod{36}$.

9. Use the method of Exercise 8 to solve $77x \equiv 14 \pmod{105}$. *Hint:* First use Theorem 4.6.

5.3 The Chinese Remainder Theorem

If the modulus of a conditional congruence is composite, solution of the congruence is frequently made easier by factoring the modulus into a product of factors which are pairwise relatively prime and solving a system of simpler congruences in place of the single given congruence. The following theorem gives the details of the method.

Theorem 5.3. *If* $m = \Pi_{i=1}^{r} m_i$ *and* $(m_i, m_j) = 1$ *for* $i \neq j$, $1 \leq i \leq r$, *and* $1 \leq j \leq r$, *then any solution of* $f(x) \equiv 0 \pmod{m}$ *is a simultaneous solution of the system*

$$f(x) \equiv 0 \pmod{m_1},$$
$$f(x) \equiv 0 \pmod{m_2},$$
$$\cdots\cdots\cdots\cdots,$$
$$f(x) \equiv 0 \pmod{m_r},$$

and conversely.

PROOF. Suppose that $f(x_0) \equiv 0 \pmod{m}$. Then, since $m_i \mid m$, it is clear that $f(x_0) \equiv 0 \pmod{m_i}$ for each i. Thus, any solution of $f(x) \equiv 0 \pmod{m}$ is a solution of the system.

Now, suppose that $f(x_0) \equiv 0 \pmod{m_i}$ for each i so that x_0 is a simultaneous solution of the system. Then, $m_i \mid f(x_0)$ for each i and, since $(m_i, m_j) = 1$ for $i \neq j$, it follows from Corollary 2.14, page 26, that $m \mid f(x_0)$. Thus, $f(x_0) \equiv 0 \pmod{m}$ and x_0 is a solution of the given congruence.

In the preceding theorem, the question left unanswered is, how does one find the simultaneous solution to the system of congruences involved? This can be accomplished by first solving each congruence of the system separately, thus finding x_i such that $f(x_i) \equiv 0 \pmod{m_i}$ for each i, and then finding a simultaneous solution x_0 to the system

(1)
$$\begin{aligned} x &\equiv x_1 \pmod{m_1}, \\ x &\equiv x_2 \pmod{m_2}, \\ &\cdots\cdots\cdots, \\ x &\equiv x_r \pmod{m_r}. \end{aligned}$$

Then, since $x_0 \equiv x_i \pmod{m_i}$ for each i,

$$f(x_0) \equiv f(x_i) \equiv 0 \pmod{m_i}$$

for each i and x_0 is a solution of the system of the preceding theorem. The problem is, therefore, ultimately reduced to that of solving the linear system (1).

Differently put, the problem of solving the preceding system of linear congruences is essentially that of finding an integer x which leaves a remainder of x_1 when divided by m_1, x_2 when divided by m_2, ..., and x_r when divided by m_r. Such problems were studied in antiquity, particularly by ancient Chinese mathematicians, so the solution to the problem is called the Chinese remainder theorem.

Theorem 5.4 (The Chinese Remainder Theorem). *If $(m_i, m_j) = 1$ for $i \neq j$, then the system*

$$\begin{aligned} x &\equiv c_1 \pmod{m_1}, \\ x &\equiv c_2 \pmod{m_2}, \\ &\cdots\cdots\cdots\cdots, \\ x &\equiv c_r \pmod{m_r}, \end{aligned}$$

is solvable and the solution is unique modulo m where $m = \prod_{i=1}^{r} m_i$.

PROOF. Let $M_i = m/m_i$ for each i. Then, $m_j | M_i$ for $i \neq j$. Also, $(m_i, M_i) = 1$ by Theorem 2.12, page 26 since $(m_i, m_j) = 1$ for $i \neq j$. Since $(m_i, M_i) = 1$, the congruence

$$M_i y \equiv 1 \pmod{m_i}$$

has a solution b_i for each i. That is, for each i there exists b_i such that $M_i b_i \equiv 1 \pmod{m_i}$. Set $x_0 = \sum_{i=1}^{r} c_i M_i b_i$. Then, $x_0 \equiv c_j \pmod{m_j}$ for each j since $c_j M_j b_j \equiv c_j \pmod{m_j}$ and $M_i \equiv 0 \pmod{m_j}$ for $i \neq j$. Thus, x_0 is a solution of the system.

Now, suppose that x_1 and x_0 are any two solutions of the system. Then,

$$x_1 \equiv c_i \equiv x_0 \pmod{m_i}$$

and so $m_i | (x_1 - x_0)$ for each i. Then, since $(m_i, m_j) = 1$ for $i \neq j$, it follows from Corollary 2.14, page 26, that $m | (x_1 - x_0)$ and $x_1 \equiv x_0 \pmod{m}$. Therefore, if a solution exists, it is unique modulo m.

The proof of the Chinese remainder theorem is constructive and, therefore, provides a method for solving a system of congruences.

EXAMPLE 5.3. Find the simultaneous solution of the system $x \equiv 1 \pmod 2$, $x \equiv 2 \pmod 3$, $x \equiv 1 \pmod 5$, and $x \equiv 5 \pmod 7$.

Solution. Here, we have

$$
\begin{aligned}
m_1 &= 2, & M_1 &= 105, & c_1 &= 1, \\
m_2 &= 3, & M_2 &= 70, & c_2 &= 2, \\
m_3 &= 5, & M_3 &= 42, & c_3 &= 1, \\
m_4 &= 7, & M_4 &= 30, & c_4 &= 5,
\end{aligned}
$$

and we must solve $M_i y \equiv 1 \pmod{m_i}$ for each i. The first congruence, $105y \equiv 1 \pmod 2$, reduces to $y \equiv 1 \pmod 2$ and so $b_1 = 1$. Similarly, $70y \equiv 1 \pmod 3$ reduces to $y \equiv 1 \pmod 3$ and so $b_2 = 1$ also. $42y \equiv 1 \pmod 5$ reduces to $2y \equiv 1 \pmod 5$ and $b_3 = 3$. Finally, $30y \equiv 1 \pmod 7$ reduces to $2y \equiv 1 \pmod 7$ and $b_4 = 4$. Thus, the desired solution is

$$
x_0 = \sum_{i=1}^{4} c_i b_i M_i = 971.
$$

This solution is unique modulo $210 = 2 \cdot 3 \cdot 5 \cdot 7$, which is to say, that any other solution differs from 971 by some multiple of 210 and, conversely, that any number which differs from 971 by a multiple of 210 is a solution. Thus, for example, the least positive solution would be $131 = 971 - 4 \cdot 210$.

An alternative and easier solution of this problem runs as follows. It is clear that $x = 1$ is a solution of the first and third congruences of the system. Also, since the solution of these two congruences is unique modulo 10, by the Chinese remainder theorem, any other solution must be of the form $1 + 10y$ for some integer y. Now, a number of this form will also be a solution of $x \equiv 2 \pmod 3$, provided that

$$
1 + 10y \equiv 2 \pmod 3.
$$

Solving this congruence for y, we obtain

$$
\begin{aligned}
10y &\equiv 1 \pmod 3, \\
y &\equiv 1 \pmod 3.
\end{aligned}
$$

Thus, $1 + 10y = 11$ is a solution of the first three congruences of the system. Since the solution of these congruences is unique modulo 30, $11 + 30z$ satisfies the first three congruences for any integer z. Hence, to find a simultaneous solution to the complete system, we seek z such that

$$
11 + 30z \equiv 5 \pmod 7.
$$

We have

$$
\begin{aligned}
30z &\equiv -6 \pmod 7, \\
2z &\equiv -6 \pmod 7, \\
z &\equiv -3 \equiv 4 \pmod 7.
\end{aligned}
$$

Thus, $11 + 30z = 131$ is a solution of the system and any other solution is congruent to this one modulo 210.

The Chinese remainder theorem is a special case of the following result which we state without proof.

Theorem 5.5. *The system*

$$x \equiv c_1 \ (mod \ m_1),$$
$$x \equiv c_2 \ (mod \ m_2),$$
$$\cdots \cdots \cdots,$$
$$x \equiv c_r \ (mod \ m_r),$$

is solvable if and only if $(m_i, m_j) \mid (c_i - c_j)$ for each i and j with $i \neq j$. If there is a solution, it is unique modulo $m = [m_1, m_2, \ldots, m_r]$.

EXAMPLE 5.4. Find the simultaneous solution of the system $x \equiv 1 \pmod{2}$, $x \equiv 2 \pmod{3}$, $x \equiv 1 \pmod{5}$, $x \equiv 5 \pmod{7}$, $x \equiv 2 \pmod{9}$.

Solution. This system, which differs from the one of Example 5.3 only in the addition of the congruence $x \equiv 2 \pmod{9}$, clearly satisfies the conditions of Theorem 5.5. Thus, it has a unique solution modulo 630, the least common multiple of the moduli involved. From Example 5.3, we have that any number of the form $131 + 210y$ satisfies the first four congruences of the system. Therefore, it is only necessary to find y such that

$$131 + 210y \equiv 2 \pmod{9}.$$

This reduces to

$$3y \equiv -3 \pmod{9}$$

and $y = -1$ is an obvious solution. Thus, $131 - 210 = -79$ is a solution of the given system. The least positive solution is $-79 + 630 = 551$.

EXAMPLE 5.5. Find the simultaneous solution of the system $5x \equiv 2 \pmod{3}$, $2x \equiv 4 \pmod{10}$, $4x \equiv 7 \pmod{9}$.

Solution. Neither Theorem 5.4 nor Theorem 5.5 apply directly to the system as given. However, the general remarks about solution of systems which preceded the Chinese remainder theorem do apply. Accordingly, we first solve each congruence separately, obtaining 1 as a solution of the first congruence, 2 and 7 as incongruent solutions of the second congruence, and 4 as the solution of the last. Now, using the Chinese remainder theorem, we solve the *two* systems

$$\left. \begin{array}{l} x \equiv 1 \ (mod \ 3), \\ x \equiv 2 \ (mod \ 10), \\ x \equiv 4 \ (mod \ 9), \end{array} \right\} \quad \text{and} \quad \left\{ \begin{array}{l} x \equiv 1 \ (mod \ 3), \\ x \equiv 7 \ (mod \ 10), \\ x \equiv 4 \ (mod \ 9). \end{array} \right.$$

The point is that each of the two solutions of the second congruence, when paired with the solutions of the other congruences, yields a separate solution of the original system modulo 90. The work is easily finished, as in the preceding examples, and the solutions are 22 and 67. These solutions are unique modulo 90.

Exercises

1. Find the least positive integer which leaves remainders of 2, 3, and 2 when divided by 3, 5, and 7, respectively. Obtain the solution in two different ways.

2. Find the integer x such that $-2310 \le x \le 2310$, and

$$x \equiv 1 \pmod{21},$$
$$x \equiv 2 \pmod{20},$$
$$x \equiv 3 \pmod{11}.$$

3. Find the least positive integer which leaves remainders of 1, 1, 4, and 3 when divided by 2, 3, 5, and 4, respectively.

4. Find the simultaneous solution of the system

$$3x \equiv 7 \pmod{5},$$
$$x \equiv 1 \pmod{4},$$
$$5x \equiv 2 \pmod{11}.$$

Suggestion: Use the method discussed immediately following the proof of Theorem 5.3.

5. Solve the system
$$2x \equiv 5 \pmod{7},$$
$$4x \equiv 2 \pmod{6},$$
$$x \equiv 3 \pmod{5}.$$

There will be two incongruent solutions modulo $210 = [7, 6, 5]$; find both of them.

6. Solve the following congruences using the method of Theorem 5.3 *et seq.* Note that there are six incongruent solutions of (d).

(a) $371x \equiv 287 \pmod{460}$
(b) $2837x \equiv 1601 \pmod{1710}$
(c) $1663x \equiv 2571 \pmod{7735}$
(d) $606x \equiv 138 \pmod{1710}$

7. Let $f(x)$ be a polynomial with integral coefficients. If

$$f(1) \equiv 0 \pmod{2},$$
$$f(2) \equiv 0 \pmod{3},$$
$$f(3) \equiv 0 \pmod{4},$$

and

$$f(4) \equiv 0 \pmod{5},$$

find a solution of the congruence $f(x) \equiv 0 \pmod{60}$.

8. Find five consecutive positive integers such that the first is divisible by 2, the second is divisible by 3, the third is divisible by 5, the fourth is divisible by 7, and the fifth is divisible by 11. *Suggestion:* Use the Chinese remainder theorem.

9. Prove that for any positive integer n, there exist n consecutive positive integers $a_1, a_2, \ldots, a_n$ such that $p_i \mid a_i$ for each i, where p_i denotes the ith prime.

10. Recall that an integer is said to be square-free if it is not divisible by the square of any prime. Prove that for any positive integer n, there exist n consecutive nonsquare-free positive integers.

11. Generalize Exercise 10 to apply to kth powers instead of squares.

5.4 Polynomial Congruences of Degree Greater Than One

Throughout this section, $f(x)$ will denote a polynomial of degree $n \geq 2$ with integral coefficients. Our purpose is to develop methods for solving the conditional congruence $f(x) \equiv 0 \pmod{m}$, where $m = \prod_{i=1}^{r} p_i^{\alpha_i}$ with $\alpha_i \geq 1$ for each i is the canonical representation of m.

If we set $m_i = p_i^{\alpha_i}$ for $i = 1, 2, \ldots, r$, it is clear from Theorem 5.3 that the solution of $f(x) \equiv 0 \pmod{m}$ is equivalent to the simultaneous solution of the system

$$f(x) \equiv 0 \pmod{p_1^{\alpha_1}},$$
$$f(x) \equiv 0 \pmod{p_2^{\alpha_2}},$$
$$\cdots \cdots \cdots \cdots,$$
$$f(x) \equiv 0 \pmod{p_r^{\alpha_r}}.$$

We have already seen that the solution of such a system can be effected by solving each of the congruences separately, and then using the Chinese remainder theorem. Thus, the problem reduces to one of solving congruences of the form $f(x) \equiv 0 \pmod{p^\alpha}$. The next two theorems show how this can be accomplished.

Theorem 5.6. *If* $f(x) = \sum_{k=0}^{n} a_k x^k$ *is a polynomial with integral coefficients, then*

$$f(a + b) = f(a) + bf'(a) + b^2 q,$$

where a, b, and q are integers and

$$f'(a) = \sum_{k=1}^{n} k a_k a^{k-1}.$$

PROOF. By the binomial theorem, for $k > 1$,

$$(a + b)^k = a^k + kba^{k-1} + b^2 q_k,$$

where

$$q_k = \sum_{i=2}^{k} \binom{k}{i} a^{k-i} b^{i-2}$$

is an integer depending on a, b, and k. Therefore,

$$f(a + b) = \sum_{k=0}^{n} a_k(a + b)^k$$

$$= \sum_{k=2}^{n} a_k(a^k + kba^{k-1} + b^2 q_k) + a_1(a + b) + a_0$$

$$= \sum_{k=0}^{n} a_k a^k + b \sum_{k=1}^{n} k a_k a^{k-1} + b^2 \sum_{k=2}^{n} a_k q_k$$

$$= f(a) + bf'(a) + b^2 q$$

where $q = \sum_{k=2}^{n} a_k q_k$ is an integer since a_k and q_k are integers for each k.

Theorem 5.7. *Let $f(x)$ be a polynomial with integral coefficients, let p be a prime, and let $\alpha \geq 2$ be an integer. Then, x_0 is a solution of $f(x) \equiv 0 \pmod{p^\alpha}$ if and only if*

$$x_0 = a + y_0 p^{\alpha-1},$$

where a is a solution of $f(x) \equiv 0 \pmod{p^{\alpha-1}}$ and y_0 is a solution of

$$\frac{f(a)}{p^{\alpha-1}} + yf'(a) \equiv 0 \pmod{p}.$$

It suffices to take $0 \leq a < p^{\alpha-1}$ and $0 \leq y_0 < p$.

PROOF. Since $p^{\alpha-1} \mid p^\alpha$, it follows that if x_0 is a solution of $f(x) \equiv 0 \pmod{p^\alpha}$, it is also a solution of $f(x) \equiv 0 \pmod{p^{\alpha-1}}$. Therefore,

$$x_0 = a + y_0 p^{\alpha-1},$$

where a is a solution of $f(x) \equiv 0 \pmod{p^{\alpha-1}}$, $0 \leq a < p^{\alpha-1}$, and y_0 is an integer, since every solution of $f(x) \equiv 0 \pmod{p^{\alpha-1}}$ can be represented in this way. Now, $a + y_0 p^{\alpha-1}$ will be a solution of $f(x) \equiv 0 \pmod{p^\alpha}$ if and only if $f(a + y_0 p^{\alpha-1}) \equiv 0 \pmod{p^\alpha}$. By Theorem 5.6,

$$f(a + y_0 p^{\alpha-1}) = f(a) + y_0 p^{\alpha-1} f'(a) + q y_0^2 p^{2\alpha-2},$$

where q is an integer and $2\alpha - 2 \geq \alpha$ since $\alpha \geq 2$. Thus, $a + y_0 p^{\alpha-1}$ is a solution of $f(x) \equiv 0 \pmod{p^\alpha}$ if and only if

$$f(a) + y_0 p^{\alpha-1} f'(a) + q y_0^2 p^{2\alpha-2} \equiv 0 \pmod{p^\alpha}.$$

Since $p^{2\alpha-2} \equiv 0 \pmod{p^\alpha}$, this reduces to

$$f(a) + y_0 p^{\alpha-1} f'(a) \equiv 0 \pmod{p^\alpha}.$$

Also, since $f(a) \equiv 0 \pmod{p^{\alpha-1}}$, $p^{\alpha-1} \mid f(a)$. Thus, by Theorem 4.6, page 58, we obtain

$$\frac{f(a)}{p^{\alpha-1}} + y_0 f'(a) \equiv 0 \pmod{p}.$$

Since the last two steps are reversible, we have that $a + y_0 p^{\alpha-1}$ is a solution of $f(x) \equiv 0 \pmod{p^\alpha}$ if and only if y_0 is a solution of

$$\frac{f(a)}{p^{\alpha-1}} + yf'(a) \equiv 0 \pmod{p}.$$

By Theorem 5.1, this congruence will have p incongruent solutions modulo p if $p \mid f'(a)$ and $p^\alpha \mid f(a)$; one incongruent solution modulo p if $p \nmid f'(a)$, and no solution if $p \mid f'(a)$ and $p^\alpha \nmid f(a)$.

Finally, if y_0 is an admissible value of y, then so is $y_0 + kp$ for any k. However,

$$a + (y_0 + kp)p^{\alpha-1} = a + y_0 p^{\alpha-1} + kp^\alpha \equiv a + y_0 p^{\alpha-1} \pmod{p^\alpha}$$

and so $y_0 + kp$ yields the same solution modulo p^α as y_0. Thus, it suffices to take $0 \leq y_0 < p$.

EXAMPLE 5.6. Find all solutions of $x^3 - x^2 + 7x + 1 \equiv 0 \pmod{8}$.

Solution. Of course, with such a small modulus the simplest procedure would be to try each of the numbers in the complete residue system $-3, -2, -1, 0, 1, 2, 3, 4$ in the given congruence. In this way, one quickly finds that the solutions are $-3, -1, 1,$ and 3, or that the least positive solutions are $1, 3, 5,$ and 7. However, it will be instructive to use the method of the preceding theorem. Using the theorem repeatedly, we first find the solutions of $f(x) \equiv 0 \pmod 2$, then those of $f(x) \equiv 0 \pmod 4$, and finally those of $f(x) \equiv 0 \pmod 8$, where $f(x) = x^3 - x^2 + 7x + 1$.

(i) It is clear that $x = 1$ is the only solution to $f(x) \equiv 0 \pmod 2$.

(ii) To find the solutions to $f(x) \equiv 0 \pmod 4$, we use the preceding theorem with $p = 2$, $\alpha = 2$, and $a = 1$. Thus, $a + y_0 p^{\alpha-1} = 1 + 2y_0$ will be a solution, provided that y_0 is a solution of

$$\frac{f(1)}{2} + yf'(1) \equiv 0 \pmod 2.$$

Since $f(1) = 8$ and $f'(1) = 8$, we must solve

$$4 + 8y \equiv 0 \pmod 2.$$

Clearly, $y = 0$ and $y = 1$ are both solutions and these yield the *two* solutions 1 and 3 of $f(x) \equiv 0 \pmod 4$. We must now check *each* of these solutions to see if they generate solutions of $f(x) \equiv 0 \pmod 8$.

(iii) First, take $a = 1$, $p = 2$, $\alpha = 3$. Then,

$$a + y_0 p^{\alpha-1} = 1 + 4y_0$$

is a solution of $f(x) \equiv 0 \pmod 8$, provided y_0 is a solution of

$$\frac{f(1)}{4} + yf'(1) \equiv 0 \pmod 2.$$

This reduces to

$$2 + 8y \equiv 0 \pmod 2,$$

and again $y = 0$ and $y = 1$ are both solutions. These yield 1 and 5 as solutions to $f(x) \equiv 0 \pmod 8$.

Finally, taking $a = 3$,

$$a + y_0 p^{\alpha-1} = 3 + 4y_0$$

is a solution of $f(x) \equiv 0 \pmod 8$, provided y_0 is a solution of

$$\frac{f(3)}{4} + yf'(3) \equiv 0 \pmod 2.$$

Since $f(3) = 40$ and $f'(3) = 28$, the congruence in question becomes

$$10 + 28y \equiv 0 \pmod 2$$

with $y = 0$ and $y = 1$ as solutions. These yield 3 and 7 as solutions of $f(x) \equiv 0 \pmod 8$.

EXAMPLE 5.7. Find all solutions of $x^3 - x^2 + 7x + 1 \equiv 0 \pmod{200}$.

Solution. Since $200 = 2^3 \cdot 5^2$, we seek the simultaneous solution to the system

$$f(x) \equiv 0 \pmod 8,$$
$$f(x) \equiv 0 \pmod{25},$$

where

$$f(x) = x^3 - x^2 + 7x + 1.$$

In the preceding example, we found that 1, 3, 5, and 7 are the solutions of

$$f(x) \equiv 0 \pmod 8.$$

In the same way, one can determine that 23 is the only solution of

$$f(x) \equiv 0 \pmod{25}.$$

Finally, the simultaneous solutions of the original system are found by using the Chinese remainder theorem to solve the system

$x \equiv 1 \pmod 8,$	$x \equiv 3 \pmod 8,$
$x \equiv 23 \pmod{25},$	$x \equiv 23 \pmod{25},$
$x \equiv 5 \pmod 8,$	$x \equiv 7 \pmod 8,$
$x \equiv 23 \pmod{25},$	$x \equiv 23 \pmod{25}.$

The values 23, 73, 123, and 173 which result are the desired solutions of the given congruence, $f(x) \equiv 0 \pmod{200}$.

The preceding discussion shows that the problem of solving the polynomial congruence

$$f(x) \equiv 0 \pmod m$$

can be reduced to that of solving

$$f(x) \equiv 0 \pmod p,$$

where p is a prime. If $f(x)$ is of degree $n \geq p$, further simplification of the problem is possible since $f(x)$ can be replaced by a polynomial of degree at most $p - 1$. To see that this is so, we divide $f(x)$ by $x^p - x$, obtaining polynomials $q(x)$ and $r(x)$ with integral coefficients, where $r(x)$ is of degree at most $p - 1$, and such that

$$f(x) = q(x)(x^p - x) + r(x).$$

Since $a^p \equiv a \pmod p$ by Fermat's theorem, it follows that

$$f(a) \equiv r(a) \pmod p$$

for any integer a. Therefore, $f(a) \equiv 0 \pmod p$ if and only if $r(a) \equiv 0 \pmod p$ and one need only consider the simpler congruence $r(x) \equiv 0 \pmod p$.

Exercises

1. Solve: (a) $5x^3 - 2x + 1 \equiv 0 \pmod{343}$
         (b) $5x^3 - 2x + 1 \equiv 0 \pmod{25}$
         (c) $5x^3 - 2x + 1 \equiv 0 \pmod{8575}$
2. Solve $2x^9 + 2x^6 - x^5 - 2x^2 - x \equiv 0 \pmod 5$.
3. Solve $x^3 - 3x^2 + 27 \equiv 0 \pmod{1125}$.
4. If a is an integer and $f(x)$ is a polynomial with integral coefficients, prove that $f(a) \equiv r \pmod m$ where r is the remainder obtained when $f(x)$ is divided by $x - a$.
5. Let a be an integer and let $f(x)$ be a polynomial with integral coefficients. If
$$f(a) \equiv 0 \pmod p,$$
where p is a prime, prove that
$$f(x) \equiv (x - a)\, q(x) \pmod p$$
where $q(x)$ is the quotient obtained when $f(x)$ is divided by $x - a$. It follows that solutions of
$$f(x) \equiv 0 \pmod p$$
which are not congruent to a are also solutions of
$$q(x) \equiv 0 \pmod p.$$
6. If $f(x)$ and $q(x)$ are polynomials with integral coefficients,
$$f(2) \equiv 5 \pmod 7,$$
and
$$f(3) \equiv 2 \pmod 7,$$
determine a linear polynomial $r(x)$ such that
$$f(x) \equiv (x - 2)(x - 3)q(x) + r(x) \pmod 7$$
for integral values of x.
7. Solve the system
$$5x^2 + 4x - 3 \equiv 0 \pmod 6,$$
$$3x^2 + 10 \equiv 0 \pmod{17}.$$

5.5 Theorems of Lagrange and Wilson

Unlike polynomial equations, polynomial congruences of degree n frequently have more than n incongruent solutions. Thus, the linear congruences of Examples 5.1 and 5.2 had four and two incongruent solutions, respectively, and the cubic congruences of Examples 5.6 and 5.7 had four incongruent solutions in each case. On the other hand, if p is a prime, then the linear congruence
$$ax \equiv b \pmod p$$
has one and only one solution, except in the trivial case when $p \mid a$ and $p \mid b$. As the following theorem shows, this situation is typical of congruences with prime moduli. This theorem is the work of the eminent French mathematician, J. L. Lagrange (1736–1813).

Theorem 5.8 (Lagrange's Theorem). *If p is a prime and $f(x) = \sum_{i=0}^{n} a_i x^i$ is a polynomial of degree $n \geq 1$ with integral coefficients and with $a_n \not\equiv 0 \pmod{p}$, then $f(x) \equiv 0 \pmod{p}$ has at most n incongruent solutions modulo p.*

PROOF. For $n = 1$, we have $f(x) = a_1 x + a_0$ with $a_1 \not\equiv 0 \pmod{p}$, and so $f(x) \equiv 0 \pmod{p}$ has one and only one solution, by Theorem 5.1.

Assume that the claim of the theorem is true for any polynomial of the specified type of degree $k \geq 1$. Suppose that $f(x)$ is of degree $k + 1$ and has at least $k + 2$ incongruent solutions modulo p. Let s be one of these solutions. Then

$$f(x) = (x - s) \cdot q(x) + r,$$

where r is an integer and $q(x)$ is a polynomial of degree k with integral coefficients. Also, the leading coefficient of $q(x)$ is a_{k+1} and $a_{k+1} \not\equiv 0 \pmod{p}$. Since $q(x)$ is a polynomial of degree k of the specified type, it has, by the induction assumption, at most k incongruent roots modulo p. However,

$$(s - s) \cdot q(s) + r \equiv f(s) \equiv 0 \pmod{p}$$

and so $r \equiv 0 \pmod{p}$. Therefore, for any x we have from the above equation that

$$(x - s) \cdot q(x) \equiv f(x) \pmod{p}.$$

From this it follows that if t is any one of the incongruent solutions of the congruence $f(x) \equiv 0 \pmod{p}$ other than s, then

$$(t - s) \cdot q(t) \equiv f(t) \equiv 0 \pmod{p}.$$

Since $t \not\equiv s \pmod{p}$, this implies that

$$q(t) \equiv 0 \pmod{p}$$

so that t is a solution of $q(x) \equiv 0 \pmod{p}$. But t can be any one of the incongruent solutions of $f(x) \equiv 0 \pmod{p}$, other than s. Since these are at least $k + 1$ in number, this contradicts the fact that $q(x) \equiv 0 \pmod{p}$ has at most k solutions. Therefore, the assumption that $f(x)$ has at least $k + 2$ incongruent solutions modulo p must be false.

As a corollary to Lagrange's theorem, it is possible to deduce another important theorem which gives a necessary condition that p be a prime. The result is ascribed to John Wilson by Edward Waring in his *Meditationes Algebraicae* published in 1770, and it is still called Wilson's theorem. However, the first proof was given by Lagrange, also in 1770.

Theorem 5.9 (Wilson's Theorem). *If p is a prime, then $(p - 1)! \equiv -1 \pmod{p}$.*

PROOF. Let

$$f(x) = \prod_{i=1}^{p-1} (x - i) - (x^{p-1} - 1)$$

$$= c_{p-2} x^{p-2} + c_{p-3} x^{p-3} + \cdots + c_1 x + c_0.$$

In view of Fermat's theorem, it is clear that $f(x) \equiv 0 \pmod{p}$ has the $p-1$ incongruent solutions $1, 2, \ldots, p-1$. But this violates Lagrange's theorem unless $c_{p-2} \equiv c_{p-3} \equiv \cdots \equiv c_1 \equiv c_0 \equiv 0 \pmod{p}$. Therefore, for any integer x,

$$\prod_{i=1}^{p-1}(x-i) - (x^{p-1}-1) \equiv 0 \pmod{p}$$

and

$$\prod_{i=1}^{p-1}(x-i) \equiv x^{p-1}-1 \pmod{p}.$$

Setting $x = p$, we obtain

$$(p-1)! \equiv -1 \pmod{p}$$

and the theorem is proved.

Exercises

1. Prove the converse of Wilson's theorem.
2. If p is a prime and $h+k = p-1$, prove that $h!k! \equiv (-1)^{k+1} \pmod{p}$. *Hint:* Note that $p-1 \equiv -1 \pmod{p}$, $p-2 \equiv -2 \pmod{p}, \ldots, (p-k) \equiv -k \pmod{p}$ and use Wilson's theorem.
3. If p is an odd prime, show that $x^2 \equiv 1 \pmod{p}$ has precisely two incongruent solutions modulo p.
4. If p is a prime and $p \geq 5$, use Theorem 5.1 and the result of Exercise 3 to show that the members of the set $S = \{2, 3, \ldots, p-2\}$ can be grouped into pairs a, b such that $a \not\equiv b \pmod{p}$ and $ab \equiv 1 \pmod{p}$.
5. For $p \geq 5$, it follows from Exercise 4 that $\prod_{i=2}^{p-2} i \equiv 1 \pmod{p}$. Use this fact to derive an alternative proof of Wilson's theorem. Note that $p=2$ and $p=3$ must be handled separately, as special cases.
6. Let the set $T = \{a_1, a_2, \ldots, a_{\phi(m)}\}$ with $a_i < a_{i+1}$ for each i be the reduced residue system selected from among the least residue system modulo m. Thus, $0 < a_i < m$ and $(a_i, m) = 1$ for each i. Prove that $\prod_{i=1}^{\phi(m)} a_i \equiv \pm 1 \pmod{m}$. *Suggestion:* Carefully review the proof of Wilson's theorem contained in Exercises 3, 4, and 5. It was found that, except for 1 and $p-1$, the elements of the reduced residue system $1, 2, \ldots, p-1$ could be grouped into pairs a, b such that $a \not\equiv b \pmod{p}$ and $ab \equiv 1 \pmod{p}$. Since $1 \cdot (p-1) \equiv -1 \pmod{p}$, it followed that $\prod_{i=1}^{p-1} i \equiv -1 \pmod{p}$. If $a = 1$ or $a = p-1$, there still exists b such that $ab \equiv 1 \pmod{p}$, but in each of these cases $b = a$. Adjust this proof to fit the present situation. Use Theorem 5.1 to show that for each i there exists j such that $a_i a_j \equiv 1 \pmod{m}$. If $j \neq i$, there is no difficulty. If $j = i$, then $a_i^2 \equiv 1 \pmod{m}$ and, by Exercise 3, Section 4.4,

$$a_{\phi(m)-i+1}^2 = (m-a_i)^2 \equiv 1 \pmod{m}.$$

Therefore, for the pair $a_i, a_{\phi(m)-i+1}$ we have that

$$a_i a_{\phi(m)-i+1} = a_i(m-a_i) \equiv -a_i^2 \equiv -1 \pmod{m}.$$

Fill in the details and make the desired conclusion.

7. If p is an odd prime and $\alpha \geq 1$ is an integer, prove that $x^2 \equiv 1 \pmod{p^\alpha}$ has precisely two incongruent solutions modulo p^α. *Hint:* From $x^2 \equiv 1 \pmod{p^\alpha}$ it follows that $(x - 1)(x + 1) \equiv 0 \pmod{p^\alpha}$.

8. Prove that $x^2 \equiv 1 \pmod{2^\alpha}$ has one incongruent solution modulo 2^α if $\alpha = 1$, two incongruent solutions modulo 2^α if $\alpha = 2$, and four incongruent solutions modulo 2^α if α is an integer greater than 2. *Suggestion:* Use mathematical induction to show that the solutions are 1, $2^{\alpha-1} - 1$, $2^{\alpha-1} + 1$, and $2^\alpha - 1$ for $\alpha \geq 3$.

9. If $m = 2^\alpha p_1^{\alpha_1} p_2^{\alpha_2} \cdots p_r^{\alpha_r}$, with $\alpha_i \geq 1$ for each i, is the canonical representation of m, prove that $x^2 \equiv 1 \pmod{m}$ has 2^r incongruent solutions modulo m if $\alpha = 0$ or $\alpha = 1$, 2^{r+1} incongruent solutions modulo m if $\alpha = 2$, and 2^{r+2} incongruent solutions modulo m if α is an integer and $\alpha > 2$.

10. Let $T = \{a_1, a_2, \ldots, a_{\phi(m)}\}$ as in Exercise 6. Deduce from Exercises 6 and 9 that $\prod_{i=1}^{\phi(m)} a_i \equiv -1 \pmod{m}$ if $m = 4$, $m = p^\alpha$, or $m = 2p^\alpha$, where p is an odd prime and that $\prod_{i=1}^{\phi(m)} a_i \equiv 1 \pmod{m}$ if m is any other positive integer. This generalization of Wilson's theorem is due to Gauss.

5.6 Quadratic Congruences

Suppose we want to solve the quadratic congruence

$$ax^2 + bx + c \equiv 0 \pmod{m}.$$

As we have seen in the general case, the solution of such a problem ultimately depends on the solution of congruences of the form

$$ax^2 + bx + c \equiv 0 \pmod{p},$$

where p is a prime. For small values of p, such congruences are easily solved by trial and error. But, if p is very large, more sophisticated methods will be needed.

Suppose, then, that p is odd and that $(a, p) = 1$. Since $(4, p) = 1$, it follows that $(4a, p) = 1$. Therefore, the solution of $ax^2 + bx + c \equiv 0 \pmod{p}$ is equivalent to the solution of $4a^2x^2 + 4abx + 4ac \equiv 0 \pmod{p}$, which can be rewritten in the form $(2ax + b)^2 \equiv (b^2 - 4ac) \pmod{p}$. This congruence can be solved if and only if we can find an integer x_0 which is a solution of $2ax + b \equiv y_0 \pmod{p}$, where y_0 is a solution of $y^2 \equiv b^2 - 4ac \pmod{p}$. Since $(2a, p) = 1$, the first of these congruences is always solvable. Thus, the solution depends on the solvability of a congruence of the form $y^2 \equiv k \pmod{p}$. If $k \equiv 0 \pmod{p}$, the congruence is trivially solvable. We now consider the case $k \not\equiv 0 \pmod{p}$.

Definition 5.1. Let p be an odd prime with $(n, p) = 1$. If the congruence $x^2 \equiv n \pmod{p}$ is solvable, then n is called a *quadratic residue* modulo p. Otherwise, n is called a *quadratic nonresidue* modulo p.

It is apparent from the definition that the quadratic residues modulo p are, essentially, the squares modulo p. Thus, 1 and 4 are quadratic residues modulo

5; 1, 4, and 2 are quadratic residues modulo 7; and a^2 is a quadratic residue modulo any odd prime p, provided $(a, p) = 1$.

The following notational device, due to Legendre, is very useful in the study of quadratic residues.

Definition 5.2. For p an odd prime and $(n, p) = 1$, we define the Legendre symbol $\left(\dfrac{n}{p}\right)$ by the equations

$$\left(\frac{n}{p}\right) = \quad 1 \text{ if } n \text{ is a quadratic residue modulo } p,$$
$$= -1 \text{ if } n \text{ is a quadratic nonresidue modulo } p.$$

In terms of the Legendre symbol, we have that $\left(\dfrac{1}{5}\right) = \left(\dfrac{4}{5}\right) = 1$, that $\left(\dfrac{2}{5}\right) = \left(\dfrac{3}{5}\right) = -1$, and that $\left(\dfrac{a^2}{p}\right) = 1$ for any odd prime p, provided $(a, p) = 1$. Moreover, if $n \equiv m \pmod{p}$, it is clear that $x^2 \equiv n \pmod{p}$ is solvable if and only if $x^2 \equiv m \pmod{p}$ is solvable. This last statement serves as the proof of the theorem which we now state.

Theorem 5.10. *Let p be an odd prime with $(n, p) = (m, p) = 1$. If $n \equiv m \pmod{p}$, then $\left(\dfrac{n}{p}\right) = \left(\dfrac{m}{p}\right)$.*

In view of the preceding theorem, it is only necessary to determine the quadratic character of each of the numbers in a reduced residue system modulo p in order to know the quadratic character of any integer n. Thus, when determining quadratic residues, one usually lists only those in the system $1, 2, \ldots, p - 1$. Also, when we say in the next theorem that there are precisely $(p - 1)/2$ quadratic residues modulo p, we mean that there are $(p - 1)/2$ quadratic residues in any reduced residue system modulo p.

Theorem 5.11. *There are precisely $(p - 1)/2$ incongruent quadratic residues modulo p where p is an odd prime.*

PROOF. We determine the number of integers n with $(n, p) = 1$ for which $x^2 \equiv n \pmod{p}$ is solvable by seeing how many different values of n we can generate by taking different values of x. In the first place, if $x^2 \equiv n \pmod{p}$ and $(n, p) = 1$, then $(x, p) = 1$. Therefore, since $x^2 \equiv y^2 \pmod{p}$ if $x \equiv y \pmod{p}$, it is clear that we need to consider only those values of x in the reduced residue system $1, 2, \ldots, p - 1$. Moreover, $(p - x)^2 \equiv x^2 \pmod{p}$ so that the squares of the numbers in the two sets $1, 2, \ldots, (p - 1)/2$ and $(p + 1)/2, \ldots, p - 1$ are congruent in pairs, and we can further restrict our attention to the first of these sets. But the squares $1^2, 2^2, \ldots, (p - 1)^2/4$ are all incongruent modulo p. If this were not the case, a congruence of the form $x^2 \equiv n \pmod{p}$ would have at least four incongruent solutions, a contradiction to Lagrange's theorem. Thus, there are precisely $(p - 1)/2$ incongruent quadratic residues modulo p and any quadratic residue is congruent to one of the numbers $1^2, 2^2, \ldots, (p - 1)^2/4$.

5.7 The Quadratic Reciprocity Law of Gauss

According to the last theorem of the preceding section, any quadratic residue modulo 7 must be congruent to one of the numbers $1^2, 2^2, 3^2$. Thus, the quadratic residues in the reduced residue system $1, 2, \ldots, 6$ are 1, 4, and 2, as noted above. Modulo 17, the quadratic residues would be 1, 4, 9, 16, 8, 2, 15, and 13. In the same way, one could find the quadratic residues modulo any odd prime p, but it is clear that the work involved would be prohibitive if p is large. The following remarkable sequence of theorems, which culminates in the famous *law of quadratic reciprocity* of Gauss, provides a more practicable method of determining the quadratic character of any particular integer n.

Discovered independently by Euler and Legendre in about 1785, the quadratic reciprocity law was rediscovered by Gauss in 1795 when he was only 18. The first proof of the result was given by Gauss, who writes of his initial effort: "For a whole year this theorem tormented me and absorbed my greatest efforts until, at last, I obtained a proof . . . ." Eventually, Gauss devised seven different proofs and later researchers have added many more. Those of Gauss, however, seem to be the most basic. The proof offered here is essentially due to Gauss and depends on Gauss's lemma which is an ingenious transformation of the following criterion of Euler.

Theorem 5.12 (Euler's Criterion). *If p is an odd prime and $(p, n) = 1$, then*

$$\left(\frac{n}{p}\right) \equiv n^{(p-1)/2} \pmod{p}.$$

PROOF. By Theorem 5.1, if $1 \leq r \leq p - 1$, there exists s with $1 \leq s \leq p - 1$ such that $rs \equiv n \pmod{p}$. If n is a quadratic nonresidue modulo p, then $r \neq s$ and the numbers $1, 2, \ldots, p - 1$ can be grouped into $(p - 1)/2$ pairs r_i, s_i such that $r_i s_i \equiv n \pmod{p}$ for $i = 1, 2, \ldots, (p - 1)/2$. Taking the product of these congruences, we obtain, by Wilson's theorem,

$$-1 \equiv (p - 1)! \equiv n^{(p-1)/2} \pmod{p}.$$

But $\left(\dfrac{n}{p}\right) = -1$ and so

$$\left(\frac{n}{p}\right) \equiv n^{(p-1)/2} \pmod{p}$$

as desired.

On the other hand, if n is a quadratic residue modulo p then, for some pair r_0, s_0, we have that $r_0 = s_0$ and $r_0^2 \equiv n \pmod{p}$. Moreover, we have already seen that

$$(p - r_0)^2 \equiv r_0^2 \equiv n \pmod{p}$$

and, by Lagrange's theorem, these are the only solutions to $x^2 \equiv n \pmod{p}$. Thus, excluding r_0 and $p - r_0$ from consideration, the other $p - 3$ numbers in the set $1, 2, \ldots, p - 1$ can again be grouped into $(p - 3)/2$ pairs r_i, s_i for which $r_i s_i \equiv n \pmod{p}$ with $r_i \neq s_i$ for $i = 1, 2, \ldots, (p - 3)/2$. Taking the

es and multiplying both sides of the result by ... ilson's theorem,

$$(p-1)! \equiv r_0(p-r_0)n^{(p-3)/2}$$
$$\equiv -r_0^2 n^{(p-3)/2}$$
$$\equiv -n^{(p-1)/2} \pmod{p}$$

). Thus, $n^{(p-1)/2} \equiv 1 \pmod{p}$ and again

$$\left(\frac{n}{p}\right) \equiv n^{(p-1)/2} \pmod{p}$$

... is an odd prime, $n = \Pi_{i=1}^{s} m_i$, and $(m_i, p) = 1$ for each

$$\left(\frac{n}{p}\right) = \prod_{i=1}^{s} \left(\frac{m_i}{p}\right).$$

PROOF. Since $(m_i, p) = 1$ for each i, it follows from Theorem 2.12, page 26, that $(n, p) = 1$. Therefore, by Euler's criterion

$$\left(\frac{n}{p}\right) \equiv n^{(p-1)/2} \equiv \prod_{i=1}^{s} m_i^{(p-1)/2} \equiv \prod_{i=1}^{s} \left(\frac{m_i}{p}\right) \pmod{p},$$

and

$$\left(\frac{n}{p}\right) - \prod_{i=1}^{s} \left(\frac{m_i}{p}\right) = kp$$

for some integer k. But, by definition of the Legendre symbol, the only possible values for the left side of this equality are ± 2 or 0. Since p is an odd prime, it must be the case that $k = 0$ and

$$\left(\frac{n}{p}\right) = \prod_{i=1}^{s} \left(\frac{m_i}{p}\right)$$

as claimed.

If $n = \Pi_{i=1}^{r} p_i^{\alpha_i}$ with $\alpha_i \geq 1$ for each i is the canonical representation of n and if p is an odd prime with $(n, p) = 1$, it follows immediately from the preceding corollary that

$$\left(\frac{n}{p}\right) = \prod_{i=1}^{r} \left(\frac{p_i}{p}\right)^{\alpha_i}.$$

Thus, the problem of determining the quadratic character of n with respect to p reduces to that of determining the quadratic character of each prime divisor of n with respect to p. This is the object of the next two theorems of Gauss.

Theorem 5.14 (Gauss's Lemma). *Let p be an odd prime and n an integer with $(n, p) = 1$. Let S denote the set of least positive residues of the integers n, $2n, \ldots, \frac{1}{2}(p - 1) \cdot n$. If r denotes the number of elements of S which exceed $p/2$, then $\left(\dfrac{n}{p}\right) = (-1)^r$.*

PROOF. Define s by $r + s = (p - 1)/2$ and denote the elements of S by $a_1, a_2, \ldots, a_s, b_1, b_2, \ldots, b_r$, where $a_i < p/2$ for each i and $b_j > p/2$ for each j. Since the elements of S are the least residues of $n, 2n, \ldots, \frac{1}{2}(p - 1) \cdot n$, it follows that

$$(2) \qquad \prod_{i=1}^{s} a_i \prod_{j=1}^{r} b_j \equiv \left(\frac{p - 1}{2}\right)! \, n^{(p-1)/2} \pmod{p}.$$

Since $p/2 < b_j < p$, it follows that $0 < p - b_j < p/2$ for each j. Moreover, $a_i \neq p - b_j$ for any i and j. To see that this is so, suppose that $a_i = p - b_j$ for some i and j. Then,

$$(h + k)n \equiv hn + kn \equiv a_i + b_j \equiv p \equiv 0 \pmod{p}$$

for some integers h, k with $h \neq k$, $1 \leq h \leq (p - 1)/2$, $1 \leq k \leq (p - 1)/2$. This implies that $p \mid (h + k)n$ and, since $(p, n) = 1$, that $p \mid (h + k)$. However, this is impossible since $0 < h + k < p$. It follows that the $(p - 1)/2$ integers $a_1, a_2, \ldots, a_s, p - b_1, \ldots, p - b_r$ are all distinct and satisfy the inequality $1 \leq x \leq (p - 1)/2$. Hence, they must be just the integers $1, 2, \ldots, (p - 1)/2$ in some order. Therefore, using (2) above, we obtain

$$\left(\frac{p - 1}{2}\right)! \equiv \prod_{i=1}^{s} a_i \prod_{j=1}^{r} (p - b_j)$$

$$(3) \qquad\qquad \equiv (-1)^r \prod_{i=1}^{s} a_i \prod_{j=1}^{r} b_j$$

$$\equiv (-1)^r \left(\frac{p - 1}{2}\right)! \, n^{(p-1)/2} \pmod{p}.$$

Since it is clearly relatively prime to p, we may divide both sides of (3) by $\left(\dfrac{p - 1}{2}\right)!$ to obtain

$$(4) \qquad\qquad 1 \equiv (-1)^r n^{(p-1)/2} \pmod{p}.$$

Multiplying both sides of (4) by $(-1)^r$ and using Euler's criterion, we obtain

$$(5) \qquad\qquad (-1)^r \equiv n^{(p-1)/2} \equiv \left(\frac{n}{p}\right) \pmod{p}.$$

Therefore, $(-1)^r - \left(\dfrac{n}{p}\right) = tp$ for some integer t. But, since the left-hand side of this last equality must equal ± 2 or 0 by definition of $\left(\dfrac{n}{p}\right)$, it follows that $t = 0$ and $\left(\dfrac{n}{p}\right) = (-1)^r$ as we wished to prove.

Definition 5.3. If α is a real number, then $[\alpha]$ denotes the *greatest integer not exceeding* α. Alternatively, $[\alpha]$ is the integer satisfying the inequality

$$[\alpha] \leq \alpha < [\alpha] + 1.$$

Theorem 5.15 (The Quadratic Reciprocity Law of Gauss). *If p and q are distinct odd primes, then*

$$\left(\frac{p}{q}\right)\left(\frac{q}{p}\right) = (-1)^{\frac{1}{2}(p-1)\cdot\frac{1}{2}(q-1)}.$$

PROOF. The proof depends on Gauss's lemma. Consider the integers q, $2q, \ldots, \frac{1}{2}(p-1) \cdot q$. For $1 \leq k \leq (p-1)/2$, let $kq = pq_k + t_k$ with q_k and t_k integers such that $1 \leq t_k \leq p-1$. Thus, t_k is the least residue of kq modulo p. Also, since

$$q_k < \frac{kq}{p} = q_k + \frac{t_k}{p} < q_k + 1,$$

it follows from Definition 5.3, that $q_k = [kq/p]$. Let $a_1, a_2, \ldots, a_s$ denote those values of t_k which are less than $p/2$ and let $b_1, b_2, \ldots, b_r$ denote those values of t_k which exceed $p/2$. Then, by Gauss's lemma, $\left(\frac{q}{p}\right) = (-1)^r$.

Let $a = \sum_{i=1}^{s} a_i$ and $b = \sum_{j=1}^{r} b_j$ so that

$$(6) \qquad a + b = \sum_{i=1}^{s} a_i + \sum_{j=1}^{r} b_j = \sum_{k=1}^{(p-1)/2} t_k.$$

As in the proof of Gauss's lemma, the numbers $a_1, \ldots, a_s, p - b_1, \ldots, p - b_r$ are just the numbers $1, 2, \ldots, (p-1)/2$ in some order. Therefore,

$$(7) \qquad \begin{aligned} a + rp - b &= \sum_{i=1}^{s} a_i + \sum_{j=1}^{r} (p - b_j) \\ &= \sum_{k=1}^{(p-1)/2} k = \frac{p^2 - 1}{8}. \end{aligned}$$

Moreover, summing the equations $kq = pq_k + t_k$ and using (6), we obtain

$$(8) \qquad \begin{aligned} p \sum_{k=1}^{(p-1)/2} q_k + a + b &= \sum_{k=1}^{(p-1)/2} (pq_k + t_k) \\ &= \sum_{k=1}^{(p-1)/2} kq = \frac{p^2 - 1}{8} \cdot q. \end{aligned}$$

Subtracting (7) from (8), we obtain

$$(9) \qquad p \sum_{k=1}^{(p-1)/2} q_k + 2b - rp = \frac{p^2 - 1}{8} \cdot (q - 1).$$

(Note that equation (9) has been obtained without making use of the fact that q is odd. We shall have occasion to refer to this in the proof of the next theorem.)

We now make use of the fact that q is odd and convert equation (9) into a congruence modulo 2. The point is that we eventually want to say something about $(-1)^r$, and the nature of this quantity depends on whether $r \equiv 0$ or $r \equiv 1 \pmod{2}$. Since $(p^2 - 1)/8$ is an integer and $p \equiv q \equiv 1 \pmod{2}$, (9) implies that

(10) $$\sum_{k=1}^{(p-1)/2} q_k \equiv r \pmod{2}.$$

For convenience, we let

$$u = \sum_{k=1}^{(p-1)/2} q_k = \sum_{k=1}^{(p-1)/2} [kq/p].$$

Then, from (10) and Gauss's lemma, we have that

$$\left(\frac{q}{p}\right) = (-1)^r = (-1)^u.$$

Now, if we repeat the preceding argument with the roles of p and q interchanged and let

$$v = \sum_{j=1}^{(q-1)/2} [jp/q],$$

it follows that we shall obtain $\left(\dfrac{p}{q}\right) = (-1)^v$. Therefore,

$$\left(\frac{p}{q}\right)\left(\frac{q}{p}\right) = (-1)^{u+v},$$

and the proof will be complete if we can show that

$$u + v = \tfrac{1}{2}(p - 1) \cdot \tfrac{1}{2}(q - 1).$$

Consider the set T of all elements of the form $jp - kq$ with $k = 1, 2, \ldots, \tfrac{1}{2}(p - 1)$ and $j = 1, 2, \ldots, \tfrac{1}{2}(q - 1)$. Clearly, T contains $\tfrac{1}{2}(p - 1) \cdot \tfrac{1}{2}(q - 1)$ elements. Moreover, none of the elements of T is zero. For, if $jp - kq = 0$, then $jp = kq$ and $p \mid kq$; this is impossible since $(p, q) = 1$ and $1 \leq k \leq \tfrac{1}{2}(p - 1)$. Thus, all elements of T are either positive or negative and we determine how many fall into each category. For fixed j, $jp - kq > 0$ for all values of $k = 1, 2, \ldots, x$ where x is the largest integer such that $jp > xq$. That is, for fixed j there are $x = [jp/q]$ values of k which yield positive elements of T. Therefore, the total number of positive elements of T is

$$v = \sum_{j=1}^{(q-1)/2} [jp/q].$$

Similarly,

$$u = \sum_{k=1}^{(p-1)/2} [kq/p]$$

is the number of negative elements in T. Since this accounts for all elements of T, we have $u + v = \tfrac{1}{2}(p - 1) \cdot \tfrac{1}{2}(q - 1)$ and the proof is complete.

EXAMPLE 5.8. Determine the quadratic character of 19 with respect to 283.

Solution. Since $\left(\dfrac{q}{p}\right) = \pm 1$, $\left(\dfrac{q}{p}\right)^2 = 1$ and the law of quadratic reciprocity can be put in the form

$$\left(\frac{p}{q}\right) = \left(\frac{q}{p}\right)(-1)^{\frac{1}{2}(p-1)\cdot\frac{1}{2}(q-1)}.$$

Therefore, since 19 and 283 are primes, we have that

$$\left(\frac{19}{283}\right) = \left(\frac{283}{19}\right) \cdot (-1)^{9\cdot141}$$

$$= -\left(\frac{283}{19}\right).$$

Since $283 \equiv 17 \pmod{19}$, it follows from Theorem 5.10 that

$$\left(\frac{283}{19}\right) = \left(\frac{17}{19}\right).$$

Again, by quadratic reciprocity,

$$\left(\frac{17}{19}\right) = \left(\frac{19}{17}\right)(-1)^{8\cdot9}$$

$$= \left(\frac{19}{17}\right)$$

and

$$\left(\frac{19}{17}\right) = \left(\frac{2}{17}\right)$$

since $19 \equiv 2 \pmod{17}$. Thus,

$$\left(\frac{19}{283}\right) = -\left(\frac{2}{17}\right)$$

and we have only to determine the quadratic character of 2 with respect to 17. Since $6^2 \equiv 2 \pmod{17}$,

$$\left(\frac{2}{17}\right) = 1 \quad\text{and}\quad \left(\frac{19}{283}\right) = -1.$$

Thus, 19 is a quadratic nonresidue modulo 283. Of course, since

$$\left(\frac{19}{283}\right)\left(\frac{283}{19}\right) = -1^{9\cdot141} = -1,$$

we also have immediately that 283 is also a quadratic residue modulo 19.

In the preceding example, note that the quadratic reciprocity law could not be used to evaluate $\left(\dfrac{2}{17}\right)$ since it only applies to odd primes. The following theorem makes it possible to evaluate $\left(\dfrac{2}{p}\right)$ for an odd prime p.

Theorem 5.16. *If p is an odd prime:*

$$\left(\frac{2}{p}\right) = \quad 1 \ for \ p \equiv \pm1 \ (mod \ 8),$$
$$= -1 \ for \ p \equiv \pm3 \ (mod \ 8).$$

PROOF. Recall that equation (9) in the proof of Theorem 5.15 was obtained without using the oddness of q. Thus, it is valid in case $q = 2$. Moreover, if $q = 2$, we have $1 \le kq \le p - 1$ so that $q_k = 0$ for each k. Therefore, equation (9) becomes

$$2b - rp = \frac{p^2 - 1}{8}.$$

Since $p \equiv 1 \pmod 2$, this implies that

$$r \equiv -r \equiv \frac{p^2 - 1}{8} \pmod 2$$

and so, by Gauss's lemma,

$$\left(\frac{2}{p}\right) = (-1)^r = (-1)^{(p^2-1)/8}.$$

Furthermore, since p is odd, $p \equiv \pm1$ or $p \equiv \pm3 \pmod 8$. If $p \equiv \pm1 \pmod 8$, then $p = \pm1 + 8k$ for some integer k and

$$p^2 = 1 \pm 16k + 64k^2.$$

Therefore, $(p^2 - 1)/8$ is even and

$$\left(\frac{2}{p}\right) = 1.$$

On the other hand, if $p \equiv \pm3 \pmod 8$, then $p = \pm3 + 8k$ for some integer k and

$$p^2 = 9 \pm 48k + 64k^2.$$

Therefore, $(p^2 - 1)/8$ is odd and

$$\left(\frac{2}{p}\right) = -1.$$

EXAMPLE 5.9. Evaluate $\left(\frac{2}{17}\right)$.

Solution. Since $17 \equiv 1 \pmod 8$, it follows from the preceding theorem that $\left(\frac{2}{17}\right) = 1$.

EXAMPLE 5.10. Determine the quadratic character of 42 with respect to 997.

Solution. We give only the bare essentials of the solution. The reader should be sure that he understands each step. Since $42 = 2 \cdot 3 \cdot 7$, it follows that

$$\left(\frac{42}{997}\right) = \left(\frac{2}{997}\right)\left(\frac{3}{997}\right)\left(\frac{7}{997}\right).$$

Moreover, by the preceding theorems,

$$\left(\frac{2}{997}\right) = -1, \left(\frac{3}{997}\right) = \left(\frac{997}{3}\right) = \left(\frac{1}{3}\right) = 1, \left(\frac{7}{997}\right) = \left(\frac{997}{7}\right) = \left(\frac{3}{7}\right) = -1.$$

Combining these results, we obtain $\left(\frac{42}{997}\right) = 1$ so that 42 is a quadratic residue modulo 997.

EXAMPLE 5.11. For what odd primes p is 3 a quadratic residue?
   Solution. By the law of quadratic reciprocity,

$$\left(\frac{3}{p}\right) = \left(\frac{p}{3}\right)(-1)^{(p-1)/2} = \quad \left(\frac{p}{3}\right) \text{ if } p \equiv 1 \ (\text{mod } 4),$$

$$= -\left(\frac{p}{3}\right) \text{ if } p \equiv 3 \ (\text{mod } 4).$$

Moreover, by Theorem 5.10, $\left(\frac{p}{3}\right) = \left(\frac{r}{3}\right)$ where r is the least residue of p modulo 3. Thus,

$$\left(\frac{p}{3}\right) = \left(\frac{1}{3}\right) = \quad 1 \text{ if } p \equiv 1 \ (\text{mod } 3),$$

$$= \left(\frac{2}{3}\right) = -1 \text{ if } p \equiv 2 \ (\text{mod } 3).$$

Hence, it follows that:

$$\left(\frac{3}{p}\right) = \quad 1 \text{ if } p \equiv 1 \ (\text{mod } 4) \text{ and } p \equiv 1 \ (\text{mod } 3),$$

$$= \quad 1 \text{ if } p \equiv 3 \ (\text{mod } 4) \text{ and } p \equiv 2 \ (\text{mod } 3),$$

$$= -1 \text{ if } p \equiv 1 \ (\text{mod } 4) \text{ and } p \equiv 2 \ (\text{mod } 3),$$

$$= -1 \text{ if } p \equiv 3 \ (\text{mod } 4) \text{ and } p \equiv 1 \ (\text{mod } 3).$$

By the Chinese remainder theorem:

$$p \equiv 1 \ (\text{mod } 4) \text{ and } p \equiv 1 \ (\text{mod } 3) \text{ imply } p \equiv 1 \ (\text{mod } 12),$$
$$p \equiv 3 \ (\text{mod } 4) \text{ and } p \equiv 2 \ (\text{mod } 3) \text{ imply } p \equiv 11 \equiv -1 \ (\text{mod } 12),$$
$$p \equiv 1 \ (\text{mod } 4) \text{ and } p \equiv 2 \ (\text{mod } 3) \text{ imply } p \equiv 5 \ (\text{mod } 12),$$
$$p \equiv 3 \ (\text{mod } 4) \text{ and } p \equiv 1 \ (\text{mod } 3) \text{ imply } p \equiv 7 \equiv -5 \ (\text{mod } 12).$$

Therefore, the above conclusion can be summarized by

$$\left(\frac{3}{p}\right) = \quad 1 \text{ if } p \equiv \pm 1 \ (\text{mod } 12),$$

$$= -1 \text{ if } p \equiv \pm 5 \ (\text{mod } 12).$$

For example, $\left(\frac{3}{37}\right) = 1$ since $37 \equiv 1 \ (\text{mod } 12)$, and $\left(\frac{3}{41}\right) = -1$ since $41 \equiv 5 \ (\text{mod } 12)$.

Exercises

1. Determine the quadratic residues modulo 11.

2. Determine the quadratic character of the following numbers modulo the prime 379. Note that 307 and 293 are primes:
   (a) 3 (b) 5 (c) 60 (d) −1 (e) 307 (f) 293

3. Let p be an odd prime. Deduce from Euler's criterion that $\left(\dfrac{-1}{p}\right) = (-1)^{(p-1)/2}$.

4. Deduce from Exercise 3 that −1 is a quadratic residue modulo an odd prime p if and only if $p \equiv 1 \pmod 4$.

5. For what odd primes p is −3 a quadratic residue? nonresidue?

6. For what odd primes p is 11 a quadratic residue? nonresidue?

7. If p and q are distinct odd primes with p or q congruent to 1 modulo 4, show that p is a quadratic residue modulo q if and only if q is a quadratic residue modulo p. *Suggestion:* Use Theorem 5.15.

8. If p and q are distinct odd primes with $p \equiv q \equiv 3 \pmod 4$, show that p is a quadratic residue modulo q if and only if q is a quadratic nonresidue modulo p.

9. Note that $2717 = 11 \cdot 13 \cdot 19$ and determine if $x^2 \equiv 295 \pmod{2717}$ is solvable.

10. Let p be an odd prime with $(a, p) = 1$ and $\left(\dfrac{a}{p}\right) = 1$. Show that $x^2 \equiv a \pmod p$ has precisely two incongruent solutions modulo p.

11. If a and p are as in Exercise 10, prove that $x^2 \equiv a \pmod{p^n}$ has precisely two incongruent solutions modulo p^n for every positive integer n. *Suggestion:* Use mathematical induction.

12. Let $m = \prod_{i=1}^{r} p_i^{\alpha_i}$, with $\alpha_i \geq 1$ and $p_i \geq 3$ for each i, be the canonical representation of m and let a be relatively prime to m. Show that $x^2 \equiv a \pmod m$ is solvable if and only if $\left(\dfrac{a}{p_i}\right) = 1$ for each i.

13. Let m and a be as in Exercise 12. If $x^2 \equiv a \pmod m$ is solvable, prove that there exist precisely 2^r incongruent solutions modulo m.

14. Solve the following congruences. Note that $539 = 11 \cdot 49$.
    (a) $3x^2 + 6x + 5 \equiv 0 \pmod 7$
    (b) $3x^2 + 6x + 5 \equiv 0 \pmod{77}$
    (c) $3x^2 + 6x + 5 \equiv 0 \pmod{539}$

15. Let p be an odd prime with $(p, a) = 1$. Prove that $ax^2 + bx + c \equiv 0 \pmod p$ has two, one, or no solutions according as $b^2 - 4ac$ is a quadratic residue, is congruent to zero, or is a quadratic nonresidue modulo p.

16. Use the result of Exercise 4 to prove that, for $n > 1$, all odd prime divisors of $n^2 + 1$ are of the form $4k + 1$.

17. In Theorem 3.3, we proved that there were infinitely many primes of the form $4k + 3$. In Exercise 3 of Section 3.2 the reader was asked to show why a similar effort to prove that there are infinitely many primes of the form $4k + 1$ must fail. Modify this method of proof and, using the result of Exercise 16, show that there are infinitely many primes of the form $4k + 1$.

18. Let p be an odd prime and let S and P denote the sum and product, respectively, of the quadratic residues modulo p. Prove that $S \equiv 0 \pmod p$ if $p > 3$ and that $P \equiv \pm 1 \pmod p$. In particular, show that $P \equiv 1 \pmod p$ if $p \equiv 3 \pmod 4$ and $P \equiv -1 \pmod p$ if $p \equiv 1 \pmod 4$. *Suggestion:* Use Exercise 2 of Section 5.5 for the result concerning P.

19. Let p be an odd prime with $(p, a) = 1$. Then, by Fermat's theorem, $a^{p-1} \equiv 1 \pmod p$. If $p - 1$ is the smallest positive value of e such that $a^e \equiv 1 \pmod p$, prove that $a^2, a^4, \ldots, a^{p-1}$ are the quadratic residues modulo p.

20. Let m be a positive odd integer, say $m = \prod_{i=1}^{r} p_i$ where the p_i are odd primes which are not necessarily distinct, and let $(n, m) = 1$. The symbol $\left(\dfrac{n}{m}\right)$, called the Jacobi symbol, is defined by the equation

$$\left(\frac{n}{m}\right) = \prod_{i=1}^{r} \left(\frac{n}{p_i}\right)$$

where $\left(\dfrac{n}{p_i}\right)$ is the Legendre symbol. Clearly, if $\left(\dfrac{n}{m}\right) = -1$, then $\left(\dfrac{n}{p_i}\right) = -1$ for some i, $x^2 \equiv n \pmod{p_i}$ is not solvable, and so $x^2 \equiv n \pmod m$ is not solvable. On the other hand, if $\left(\dfrac{n}{m}\right) = 1$, then $x^2 \equiv n \pmod m$ may or may not be solvable; we can only be sure that $\left(\dfrac{n}{p_i}\right) = -1$ for an even number of values of i. For example, $\left(\dfrac{1}{15}\right) = 1$ and $x^2 \equiv 1 \pmod{15}$ is solvable, whereas $\left(\dfrac{2}{15}\right) = 1$ and $x^2 \equiv 2 \pmod{15}$ is not solvable. Nevertheless, the Jacobi symbol is useful in determining quadratic character as the following results show.

(a) For $m > 0$, m odd, $(m, n) = 1$, and $n \equiv n' \pmod m$, prove that $\left(\dfrac{n}{m}\right) = \left(\dfrac{n'}{m}\right)$.

(b) For $m > 0$, m odd, $n = \prod_{j=1}^{s} m_j$, and $(m, m_j) = 1$ for each j, prove that

$$\left(\frac{n}{m}\right) = \prod_{j=1}^{s} \left(\frac{m_j}{m}\right).$$

Suggestion: Use Corollary 5.13.

(c) Let $m = \prod_{i=1}^{r} p_i$ where the p_i are odd primes not necessarily distinct, let $n = \prod_{j=1}^{s} q_j$ where the q_j are odd primes not necessarily distinct, and let $(m, n) = 1$. Deduce from the law of quadratic reciprocity that

$$\left(\frac{m}{n}\right)\left(\frac{n}{m}\right) = \prod_{i=1}^{r} \prod_{j=1}^{s} \left(\frac{p_i}{q_j}\right)\left(\frac{q_j}{p_i}\right)$$

$$= \prod_{i=1}^{r} \prod_{j=1}^{s} (-1)^{\frac{1}{2}(p_i-1)\cdot\frac{1}{2}(q_j-1)}$$

$$= (-1)^{\frac{1}{2}\sum_{i=1}^{r}(p_i-1)\cdot\frac{1}{2}\sum_{j=1}^{s}(q_j-1)}$$

(d) Let $a_1, a_2, \ldots, a_r$ be odd integers. Use mathematical induction to show that

$$\tfrac{1}{2} \sum_{i=1}^{r} (a_i - 1) \equiv \tfrac{1}{2}\left(\prod_{i=1}^{r} a_i - 1 \right) (\text{mod } 2)$$

for every $r \geq 2$. *Hint:* For $r = 2$, note that

$$\tfrac{1}{2}(a_1 a_2 - a_1 - a_2 + 1) = \tfrac{1}{2}(a_1 - 1)(a_2 - 1) \equiv 0 \ (\text{mod } 2)$$

so that $\tfrac{1}{2}(a_1 a_2 - 1) \equiv \tfrac{1}{2}(a_1 - 1) + \tfrac{1}{2}(a_2 - 1)(\text{mod } 2)$.

(e) Use (c) and (d) to prove that $\left(\dfrac{m}{n}\right)\left(\dfrac{n}{m}\right) = (-1)^{\frac{1}{2}(m-1)\cdot\frac{1}{2}(n-1)}$ for m and n as in (c).

(f) For $m > 0$, m odd, prove that $\left(\dfrac{2}{m}\right) = (-1)^{(m^2-1)/8}$.

(g) For $m > 0$, m odd, prove that $\left(\dfrac{-1}{m}\right) = (-1)^{(m-1)/2}$.

(h) The preceding results can often be used to shorten the computation of the quadratic character of n with respect to p. For example,

$$\left(\frac{21}{89}\right) = \left(\frac{89}{21}\right) = \left(\frac{5}{21}\right) = \left(\frac{21}{5}\right) = \left(\frac{1}{5}\right) = 1$$

so that 21 is a quadratic residue modulo the prime 89. Use (e), (f), and (g) to evaluate the following Legendre symbols:

$$\left(\frac{35}{179}\right), \left(\frac{55}{167}\right), \text{ and } \left(\frac{51}{151}\right).$$

5.8 Primitive Roots and Power Residues

In the preceding sections, we considered the problem of solving the pure quadratic congruence $x^2 \equiv n \ (\text{mod } p)$ for an odd prime p with $(p, n) = 1$. A natural extension of this investigation is to ask what happens if 2 is replaced by m, and we shall now consider the mth order congruence $x^m \equiv n \ (\text{mod } p)$.

Definition 5.4. If $x^m \equiv n \ (\text{mod } p)$ is solvable with p an odd prime, $(p, n) = 1$, and $m \geq 1$, then n is called an *mth power residue* modulo p.

Since the problem of determining mth power residues is a generalization of determining quadratic residues, it is not unreasonable to expect that the solution to the present problem might resemble that of the former. Recall that, by Euler's criterion, $\left(\dfrac{n}{p}\right) \equiv n^{(p-1)/2} \ (\text{mod } p)$. Thus, for $(p, n) = 1$, $x^2 \equiv n \ (\text{mod } p)$ is solvable if and only if $n^{(p-1)/2} \equiv 1 \ (\text{mod } p)$, and we note that $2 = (p - 1, 2)$. Similarly, suppose that a is a solution to $x^m \equiv n \ (\text{mod } p)$ and that $(p, n) = 1$. Then $(p, a) = 1$ and, by Fermat's theorem,

$$n^{(p-1)/d} \equiv a^{(p-1)m/d} \equiv 1 \ (\text{mod } p),$$

where $d = (m, p - 1)$ so that m/d is an integer. Thus, for $(p, n) = 1$, a necessary condition that $x^m \equiv n \ (\text{mod } p)$ be solvable is that

$$n^{(p-1)/d} \equiv 1 \ (\text{mod } p),$$

where $d = (p - 1, m)$. It turns out that this condition is also sufficient and so is a valid generalization of Euler's criterion.

To prove the sufficiency of the preceding condition, we first develop some general ideas concerning congruences of the type $n^k \equiv 1 \pmod{r}$ for $(n, r) = 1$. By the Euler-Fermat theorem, $n^{\phi(r)} \equiv 1 \pmod{r}$. Therefore, there exists a least positive integer k such that $n^k \equiv 1 \pmod{r}$.

Definition 5.5. If k is the least positive integer such that $n^k \equiv 1 \pmod{r}$, we say that n *belongs to the exponent k modulo r.*

Note that the preceding definition is meaningless unless $(n, r) = 1$. Thus, when we say that n belongs to k modulo r, we always imply that $(n, r) = 1$.

For an example, consider the powers of 2 modulo 7. By direct computation, we obtain

$$2 \equiv 2, \quad 2^2 \equiv 4, \quad 2^3 \equiv 1, \quad 2^4 \equiv 2, \quad 2^5 \equiv 4, \quad 2^6 \equiv 1, \quad 2^7 \equiv 2, \ldots .$$

Thus, it is apparent that 2 belongs to 3 modulo 7. Also, we note that the powers of 2 modulo 7 repeat in a cycle of 3 and that those exponents h for which $2^h \equiv 1 \pmod 7$ are multiples of 3. This is true in general, as the following theorem shows. This theorem is the key to a sequence of results which eventually culminate in the desired result concerning mth power residues.

Theorem 5.17. *If n belongs to k modulo r and $n^h \equiv 1 \pmod r$, then $k \mid h$.*

PROOF. Since n belongs to k modulo r, $n^k \equiv 1 \pmod r$ and $(n, r) = 1$. Dividing h by k, we obtain integers q and s with $0 \leq s < k$ such that $h = kq + s$. Thus,

$$n^h = n^{kq+s} = (n^k)^q n^s$$

and, since $n^h \equiv n^k \equiv 1 \pmod r$, it follows that $n^s \equiv 1 \pmod r$. But since $s < k$, this contradicts the hypothesis that n belongs to k modulo r unless $s = 0$. Therefore, $s = 0$ and $k \mid h$ as claimed.

Corollary 5.18. (i) *If n belongs to k modulo r, then $k \mid \phi(r)$.* (ii) *If n belongs to k modulo p where p is a prime, then $k \mid p - 1$.*

PROOF. This follows directly from Theorem 5.17 since $n^{\phi(r)} \equiv 1 \pmod r$ and $n^{p-1} \equiv 1 \pmod p$ by the Euler-Fermat theorem and Fermat's theorem, respectively.

Corollary 5.19. *Let n belong to k modulo r. Then $n^a \equiv n^b \pmod r$ if and only if $a \equiv b \pmod k$.*

PROOF. Suppose $a \equiv b \pmod k$. Then $a = b + kq$ for some integer q and

$$n^a = n^{b+kq} = n^b(n^k)^q \equiv n^b \pmod r,$$

since $n^k \equiv 1 \pmod r$. Conversely, suppose $n^a \equiv n^b \pmod r$. It is no restriction to assume that $b \leq a$. Since n belongs to k modulo r, $(n, r) = 1$. Therefore, $(n^b, r) = 1$ and we can divide n^b out of $n^a \equiv n^b \pmod r$ to obtain $n^{a-b} \equiv 1 \pmod r$. But then $k \mid (a - b)$ by Theorem 5.17 and so $a \equiv b \pmod k$.

Corollary 5.20. *If k is positive and n belongs to hk modulo r, then n^h belongs to k modulo r.*

PROOF. By hypothesis, $n^{hk} \equiv 1 \pmod r$. Suppose n^h belongs to e modulo r. Then, by Theorem 5.17, $e \mid k$. On the other hand, $n^{he} \equiv 1 \pmod r$ and, by the same theorem, $hk \mid he$. This implies that $k \mid e$ and so $k = e$ since both e and k are positive.

Corollary 5.21. *If n belongs to h and m belongs to k modulo r and if $(h, k) = 1$, then nm belongs to hk modulo r.*

PROOF. Suppose that nm belongs to e modulo r. Then $(nm)^e \equiv 1 \pmod r$ and $n^{he}m^{he} \equiv 1 \pmod r$. Since n belongs to h modulo r, $n^{he} \equiv 1^e \equiv 1 \pmod r$ and it follows that $m^{he} \equiv 1 \pmod r$. But m belongs to k modulo r and so, by Theorem 5.17, $k \mid he$. Since $(k, h) = 1$, this implies that $k \mid e$. Similarly, one can show that $h \mid e$. Therefore, by Theorem 2.13, page 26, $hk \mid e$. On the other hand,

$$(nm)^{hk} = (n^h)^k (m^k)^h \equiv 1 \pmod r$$

and so $e \mid hk$. Thus, $e = hk$ and the proof is complete.

Corollary 5.22. *If q belongs to $\phi(r)$ modulo r, then q, q^2, q^3, ..., $q^{\phi(r)}$ form a reduced residue system modulo r.*

PROOF. Since a reduced residue system modulo r involves $\phi(r)$ numbers, we have only to show that the numbers in the set q, q^2, ..., $q^{\phi(r)}$ are mutually incongruent modulo r. Suppose this is not so. Then there exist i and j with $1 \leq i < j < \phi(r)$ such that

$$q^j \equiv q^i \pmod r.$$

Then, by Corollary 5.19, $j \equiv i \pmod{\phi(r)}$ and $\phi(r) \mid (j - i)$. But this is impossible since $0 < j - i < \phi(r)$. Therefore, $q^j \not\equiv q^i \pmod r$ for $1 \leq i < j \leq \phi(r)$ and the proof is complete.

If q belongs to $\phi(r)$ modulo r, the preceding theorem provides a particularly neat and useful method for obtaining a reduced residue system modulo r. In view of this important property, we distinguish such values of q with a special name.

Definition 5.6. *If q belongs to $\phi(r)$ modulo r, then q is called a primitive root modulo r.*

Primitive roots do not exist for all values of r. They do exist for $r = 2$, 4, p^α, and $2p^\alpha$ where p is an odd prime, but we shall not give the proof here. We do show, however, that primitive roots exist for every odd prime p. The proof given is due to I. M. Vinogradov.

Theorem 5.23. *There exist primitive roots modulo p where p is an odd prime.*

PROOF. Since each of the numbers $1, 2, \ldots, p - 1$ satisfy Fermat's theorem, each must belong to some exponent modulo p. These exponents may not all be distinct since more than one number may belong to a given exponent. Let

$e_1, e_2, \ldots, e_t$ denote the various exponents to which $1, 2, \ldots, p-1$ belong and let $u = [e_1, e_2, \ldots, e_t]$. Let $u = \Pi_{i=1}^{s} p_i^{\alpha_i}$, with $\alpha_i \geq 1$ for each i, denote the canonical representation of u. It follows from Theorem 2.22, page 35, that, for each i, there exists a corresponding j such that $p_i^{\alpha_i} | e_j$, say $e_j = q_i p_i^{\alpha_i}$. Let x_i be one of the numbers from among $1, 2, \ldots, p-1$ which belongs to e_j. Then $x_i^{q_i}$ belongs to $p_i^{\alpha_i}$ by Corollary 5.20. Therefore, it follows from Corollary 5.21 that $x = \Pi_{i=1}^{s} x_i^{q_i}$ belongs to u modulo r. But, since $e_j | u$ for each j and $e_1, e_2, \ldots, e_t$ are the exponents to which $1, 2, \ldots, p-1$ belong, it follows that

$$x^u \equiv 1 \ (\text{mod } p)$$

is satisfied by each of the numbers $1, 2, \ldots, p-1$. Therefore, it follows from Lagrange's theorem that $u \geq p-1$. On the other hand, $e_j | p-1$ for each j by Corollary 5.18. Thus, again by Theorem 2.22, $u | (p-1)$ and we have $u \leq p-1$. Therefore, $u = p-1$ and, since x belongs to u modulo r, the proof is complete.

We are now in a position to prove the aforementioned generalization of Euler's criterion for mth power residues modulo an odd prime p.

Lemma 5.24. *Let p be an odd prime with $(p, n) = 1$ and let q be a primitive root modulo p. Then $x^m \equiv n \ (\text{mod } p)$ is solvable if and only if $n \equiv q^{kd} \ (\text{mod } p)$ where k is an integer and $d = (p-1, m)$.*

PROOF. Since q is a primitive root modulo p, it follows from Corollary 5.22 with $r = p$, that the powers $q, q^2, \ldots, q^{p-1}$ form a reduced residue system modulo p. Therefore, since $(n, p) = 1$, $n \equiv q^a \ (\text{mod } p)$ for some a with $1 \leq a \leq p-1$. Moreover, any solution u of $x^m \equiv n \ (\text{mod } p)$ must also be relatively prime to p and so $u \equiv q^s \ (\text{mod } p)$ for some integer s. Therefore, $x^m \equiv n \ (\text{mod } p)$ is solvable if and only if there exists s such that

$$q^{sm} \equiv q^a \ (\text{mod } p).$$

It follows from Corollary 5.19 that this is true if and only if s satisfies $sm \equiv a \ (\text{mod } p-1)$ and, by Theorem 5.1, this is solvable for s if and only if $d | a$, say $a = kd$, where $d = (p-1, m)$. Thus $x^m \equiv n \ (\text{mod } p)$ is solvable if and only if $n = q^{kd}$ as claimed.

Theorem 5.25. *Let p be an odd prime with $(p, n) = 1$, let m be a positive integer, and let $d = (p-1, m)$. Then $x^m \equiv n \ (\text{mod } p)$ is solvable if and only if*

$$n^{(p-1)/d} \equiv 1 \ (\text{mod } p).$$

PROOF. As noted earlier, if a is a solution of $x^m \equiv n \ (\text{mod } p)$, then

$$n^{(p-1)/d} \equiv a^{(p-1)m/d} \equiv 1 \ (\text{mod } p)$$

since m/d is an integer and $(p, a) = 1$.

Conversely, suppose $n^{(p-1)/d} \equiv 1 \ (\text{mod } p)$. Then $(p, n) = 1$ and there exists some integer t such that $n \equiv q^t \pmod{p}$ where q is a primitive root modulo p. Therefore,

$$q^{t(p-1)/d} \equiv n^{(p-1)/d} \equiv 1 \pmod{p}.$$

But, since q is a primitive root modulo p, q belongs to $p - 1$ modulo p, and this implies that

$$(p - 1) \mid (p - 1) \cdot \frac{t}{d}.$$

Hence, we have that $t/d = k$ where k is an integer. But then $n \equiv q^{kd} \pmod{p}$ and $x^m \equiv n \pmod{p}$ is solvable, by Lemma 5.24.

It also follows from Lemma 5.24 that there are precisely $(p - 1)/d$ mth power residues modulo the odd prime p where $d = (p - 1, m)$. In fact, if a primitive root modulo p is known, it is possible to list the mth power residues modulo p explicitly.

Theorem 5.26. *Let p be an odd prime, let q be a primitive root modulo p, and let $d = (m, p - 1)$ where $m \geq 1$. Then the mth power residues modulo p are $q^d, q^{2d}, \ldots, q^{d \cdot (p-1)/d}$.*

PROOF. As usual, when we say that $q^d, q^{2d}, \ldots, q^{d \cdot (p-1)/d}$ are the mth power residues modulo p, we mean that these numbers are mth power residues, that they are mutually incongruent modulo p, and that any mth power residue is congruent modulo p to one of the numbers in this list.

(i) By Lemma 5.24, all the numbers in the given list are mth power residues.

(ii) Suppose that two numbers in the list are congruent modulo p. Then $q^{id} \equiv q^{jd} \pmod{p}$ for some i and j with $1 \leq j < i \leq (p - 1)/d$. Therefore, by Corollary 5.19, $(p - 1) \mid d(i - j)$. But this is impossible since

$$0 < d(i - j) < p - 1.$$

Thus, the numbers in the list are mutually incongruent modulo p.

(iii) Now, suppose a is an mth power residue modulo p. Then, by Lemma 5.24, $a = q^{kd}$ for some integer k. Let $t = (p - 1)/d$. Then, by a slight modification of Theorem 1.7, page 14, there exist s and r with $0 < r \leq t$ such that $k = st + r$. Therefore,

$$\begin{aligned} a &= q^{kd} \\ &= q^{(st+r)d} \\ &= q^{(p-1)s} q^{rd} \\ &\equiv q^{rd} \pmod{p} \end{aligned}$$

since $q^{p-1} \equiv 1 \pmod{p}$ because q is a primitive root modulo p. But, since q^{rd} is one of the numbers in the given list, this completes the proof.

EXAMPLE 5.12. Find the fourth power residues modulo 11.

Solution. It is easy to show by direct computation that 2 is a primitive root modulo 11. Thus, since $p - 1 = 10$, $m = 4$, and $d = 2$, it follows from the preceding theorem that $2^2 \equiv 4$, $2^4 \equiv 5$, $2^6 \equiv 9$, $2^8 \equiv 3$, and $2^{10} \equiv 1$ are the fourth power residues modulo 11. Of course, this is easily checked directly by computing the fourth powers of the numbers in the reduced residue system ± 1, ± 2, ± 3, ± 4, ± 5. As before, we have that $(\pm 1)^4 \equiv 1$, $(\pm 2)^4 \equiv 5$, $(\pm 3)^4 \equiv 4$, $(\pm 4)^4 \equiv 3$, and $(\pm 5)^4 \equiv 9$.

EXAMPLE 5.13. Is the congruence $x^7 \equiv 15 \pmod{29}$ solvable?

Solution. Here $n = 15$, $p - 1 = 28$, $m = 7$, and $d = 7$. To use Theorem 5.25, we check the least residue of 15^4 modulo 29. Since $15^2 \equiv -7 \pmod{29}$, $15^4 \equiv -9 \not\equiv 1 \pmod{29}$ and so $x^7 \equiv 15 \pmod{29}$ is not solvable.

Exercises

1. Find the cubic residues modulo 7.

2. Show that 2 is a primitive root modulo 29.

3. Find all seventh power residues modulo 29.

4. Find all incongruent solutions modulo 29 to $x^7 \equiv 12 \pmod{29}$. There are 7 such solutions.

5. If $n^{(p-1)/d} \equiv 1 \pmod{p}$ where p is an odd prime, $m > 0$, $(p, n) = 1$, and $d = (m, p - 1)$, prove that $x^m \equiv n \pmod{p}$ has precisely d incongruent solutions modulo p. *Hint:* Review the proof of Lemma 5.24.

6. Use Theorem 5.25 to decide if $x^5 \equiv 13 \pmod{23}$ is solvable.

7. If p is an odd prime and q is a primitive root modulo p, prove that $-q$ is a primitive root modulo p if and only if $p \equiv 1 \pmod 4$.

8. To what exponent does 2 belong modulo 7? modulo 5? modulo 35? Does this suggest a general rule? Try other examples in order to refine your guess.

9. If m belongs to h modulo r and belongs to k modulo s, and if $(r, s) = 1$, prove that m belongs to $[h, k]$ modulo rs.

10. We know that 2 belongs to 28 modulo 29. To what exponents do 2^2, 2^3, 2^4, and 2^5 belong modulo 29? Guess to what exponent 2^k belongs modulo 29 for any positive integer k.

11. If n belongs to k modulo r, prove that n^h belongs to k/d modulo r where $h > 0$ and $d = (h, k)$.

12. Use the result of the preceding exercise and Theorem 5.23 to prove that there are $\phi(p - 1)$ primitive roots modulo the odd prime p.

13. Find the $\phi(28) = 12$ primitive roots modulo 29.

14. Prove that the product of the primitive roots modulo 29 is congruent to 1 modulo 29. Do you suppose that this is generally true? Try some other examples.

15. For $p > 3$, prove that the primitive roots modulo p occur in pairs u, v such that $uv \equiv 1 \pmod{p}$. *Hint:* Note that if $(a, p - 1) = 1$, then $(p - 1 - a, p - 1) = 1$ also.

16. Prove that the product of the primitive roots modulo the prime p is congruent to 1 modulo p if $p > 3$.

17. Let q be a primitive root of the odd prime p. Prove that q is a primitive root modulo p^2 if and only if $q^{p-1} \not\equiv 1 \pmod{p^2}$.

18. Use the fact that each prime possesses a primitive root to prove Wilson's theorem. *Hint:* If q is a primitive root modulo p, then $(p - 1)! \equiv q^{1+2+\cdots+(p-1)} \pmod{p}$.

19. Let p be an odd prime and let q be a primitive root modulo p. If $n \equiv q^r \pmod{p}$, then r is called the *index of n to the base q modulo p*, and we write $r = \operatorname{ind}_q n$ modulo p. Since, by Corollary 5.22, the numbers $q, q^2, \ldots, q^{p-1}$ form a reduced residue system modulo p, it is clear that each integer relatively prime to p possesses an index to the base q modulo p. The following results show that the notion of an index to base q modulo p is analogous to that of a logarithm, even to the point of devising proofs. In each case let $(n, p) = (m, p) = 1$.

(a) Prove that $q^{\operatorname{ind}_q n} \equiv n \pmod{p}$.

(b) Prove that $\operatorname{ind}_q 1 \equiv 0 \pmod{p-1}$ and that $\operatorname{ind}_q q \equiv 1 \pmod{p-1}$.

(c) Prove that $m \equiv n \pmod{p}$ if and only if $\operatorname{ind}_q n \equiv \operatorname{ind}_q m \pmod{p-1}$.

(d) Prove that $\operatorname{ind}_q(mn) \equiv \operatorname{ind}_q m + \operatorname{ind}_q n \pmod{p-1}$.

(e) Prove that $\operatorname{ind}_q n^t \equiv t \operatorname{ind}_q n \pmod{p-1}$.

20. Tables of indices to base q modulo p are easily constructed once it is known that q is a primitive root modulo p. For example, 2 is a primitive root modulo 13. To construct a table of indices to the base 2 modulo 13, we simply compute the least residues of the powers $2, 2^2, \ldots, 2^{12}$. Since $2^1 \equiv 2$, $2^2 \equiv 4$, $2^3 \equiv 8$, $2^4 \equiv 3$, $2^5 \equiv 6$, $2^6 \equiv 12$, $2^7 \equiv 11$, $2^8 \equiv 9$, $2^9 \equiv 5$, $2^{10} \equiv 10$, $2^{11} \equiv 7$, and $2^{12} \equiv 1$, all modulo 13, it follows that $\operatorname{ind}_2 2 = 1$, $\operatorname{ind}_2 4 = 2$, and so on. This is conveniently summarized in the following table:

n	1	2	3	4	5	6	7	8	9	10	11	12
$\operatorname{ind}_2 n$	12	1	4	2	9	5	11	3	8	10	7	6

Compute a table of indices to base 2 modulo 11.

21. Indices can sometimes be used to advantage in solving conditional congruences. For example, if we presume that x is an integer which satisfies $7x \equiv 5 \pmod{13}$, then it follows from the properties in Exercise 19 that

$$\operatorname{ind}_2 7 + \operatorname{ind}_2 x \equiv \operatorname{ind}_2 5 \pmod{12}.$$

But, by the preceding table, $\operatorname{ind}_2 7 = 11$ and $\operatorname{ind}_2 5 = 9$. Therefore, x satisfies

$$11 + \operatorname{ind}_2 x \equiv 9 \pmod{12}.$$

Thus,

$$\operatorname{ind}_2 x \equiv 10 \pmod{12}$$

and, by the table of indices, we finally have that $x = 10$. Since the argument is completely reversible, 10 is the desired solution of $7x \equiv 5 \pmod{13}$.

Similarly and more concisely, we solve $x^5 \equiv 2 \pmod{13}$. Omitting the indication of base and using the preceding table, we have,

$$5 \operatorname{ind} x \equiv 1 \pmod{12},$$
$$25 \operatorname{ind} x \equiv 5 \pmod{12},$$
$$\operatorname{ind} x \equiv 5 \pmod{12},$$
$$x \equiv 6 \pmod{13}.$$

Again, the argument is reversible and $x = 6$ is the desired solution. Solve the following conditional congruences:

(a) $8x \equiv 7 \pmod{13}$

(b) $18x \equiv 14 \pmod{26}$

(c) $x^4 \equiv 9 \pmod{13}$

(d) $x^6 \equiv 12 \pmod{13}$

22. Use the theory of indices to prove Lemma 5.24.

6

Multiplicative Number-Theoretic Functions

6.1 Introduction

From time to time in the course of our discussion we have had occasion to consider functions whose domain of definition is the set of positive integers. Thus, in Section 2.5, we considered the functions $\tau(n)$ and $\sigma(n)$ which denote, respectively, the number of positive divisors and the sum of the positive divisors of the positive integer n. And, in Section 4.4, we introduced the Euler ϕ-function, $\phi(n)$, which denotes the number of positive integers not exceeding n which are relatively prime to n. Such functions, defined on the set of positive integers, are called *number-theoretic* functions.

In Section 2.5, we showed that

$$(1) \qquad \tau(n) = \prod_{i=1}^{r} (n_i + 1)$$

and

$$(2) \qquad \sigma(n) = \prod_{i=1}^{r} \frac{p_i^{n_i+1} - 1}{p_i - 1},$$

where $n = \prod_{i=1}^{r} p_i^{n_i}$ is the canonical representation of n. Suppose now that m and n are relatively prime positive integers. Then we can write $n = \prod_{i=1}^{r} p_i^{n_i}$ and $m = \prod_{j=1}^{s} q_j^{m_j}$ where the p_i and q_j are distinct primes, and it follows that

$$\tau(mn) = \prod_{j=1}^{s} (m_j + 1) \cdot \prod_{i=1}^{r} (n_i + 1) = \tau(m)\tau(n)$$

and

$$\sigma(mn) = \prod_{j=1}^{s} \frac{q_j^{m_j+1} - 1}{q_j - 1} \cdot \prod_{i=1}^{r} \frac{p_i^{n_i+1} - 1}{p_i - 1} = \sigma(m)\sigma(n).$$

Of course, it is not generally true that a function f possesses the property that $f(mn) = f(m)f(n)$ when $(m, n) = 1$. On the other hand, it is a useful property which is present sufficiently often to make the study of functions possessing the property quite worthwhile.

Definition 6.1. A number-theoretic function f is called *multiplicative* if $f(mn) = f(m)f(n)$ whenever $(m, n) = 1$. If $f(mn) = f(m)f(n)$ for all m and n, then f is said to be *completely multiplicative*.

We have just seen that the functions $\tau(n)$ and $\sigma(n)$ are *multiplicative* and the reader can easily convince himself that neither function is *completely multiplicative*. On the other hand, the functions $q(n) = 1$ for all n and $h(n) = n$ for all n are, clearly, completely multiplicative.

Our purpose in this chapter is to study multiplicative number-theoretic functions in some detail.

Exercises

1. If r is fixed, show that the function $h(n) = n^r$ is completely multiplicative.

2. Let $p(n)$ denote the number of distinct prime divisors of n. For example, $p(12) = p(24) = 2$ and $p(60) = 3$. Let $q(n) = a^{p(n)}$ where a is fixed and show that $q(n)$ is multiplicative, but not completely multiplicative.

3. If f is completely multiplicative and $m \mid n$, show that $f(n/m) = f(n)/f(m)$.

4. If f is multiplicative, $m \mid n$, and $(m, n/m) = 1$, show that $f(n/m) = f(n)/f(m)$.

5. If n is a positive integer, show that the number of positive divisors of n is odd if and only if n is a perfect square.

6.2 Notation

In the next few sections, we shall frequently want to add a number-theoretic function over the positive divisors of a positive integer n and we shall indicate this sum by writing $\sum_{d \mid n} f(d)$. Thus, for example,

$$\sum_{d \mid 1} f(d) = f(1)$$

and

$$\sum_{d \mid 6} f(d) = f(1) + f(2) + f(3) + f(6).$$

Also, $\sigma(n) = \sum_{d \mid n} d$ and $\tau(n) = \sum_{d \mid n} 1$.

Manipulating such sums can sometimes be confusing and the reader may want to prepare himself by first reviewing the formulas developed in Section 1.2. In particular, formulas (2), (2'), (4), (6), and (7) of that section would appear in the present context as follows:

$$(3) \qquad \sum_{d \mid n} kf(d) = k \cdot \sum_{d \mid n} f(d),$$

$$(4) \qquad \sum_{d \mid n} k = k \cdot \sum_{d \mid n} 1 = k \cdot \tau(n),$$

$$(5) \qquad \sum_{d \mid n} \sum_{b \mid m} f(d)g(b) = \sum_{d \mid n} \left\{ f(d) \cdot \sum_{b \mid m} g(b) \right\},$$

$$(6) \qquad \sum_{d \mid n} \sum_{b \mid m} f(d)g(b) = \sum_{d \mid n} f(d) \cdot \sum_{b \mid m} g(b),$$

$$(7) \qquad \sum_{d \mid n} \{f(d) + g(d)\} = \sum_{d \mid n} f(d) + \sum_{d \mid n} g(d).$$

Finally, we note that if d divides n, then n/d also divides n; and as d runs through the divisors of n, n/d runs through the divisors of n, in reverse order. For example, as d assumes, successively, the values 1, 2, 3, and 6, $6/d$ assumes the values 6, 3, 2, and 1. In general, we have that

(8) $$\sum_{d|n} f(d) = \sum_{d|n} f\left(\frac{n}{d}\right),$$

and this formula is frequently quite useful.

Exercises

1. Write out the following pairs of sums and show that they are equal.

(a) $\displaystyle\sum_{d|6}\sum_{b|9} f(d)g(b)$ and $\displaystyle\sum_{d|6} f(d) \cdot \sum_{b|9} g(b)$

(b) $\displaystyle\sum_{d|12}\left\{\sum_{b|(12/d)} f(d)g(b)\right\}$ and $\displaystyle\sum_{b|12}\left\{\sum_{d|(12/b)} f(d)g(b)\right\}$

2. Show that

$$\sum_{d|n}\left\{\sum_{b|(n/d)} f(d)g(b)\right\} = \sum_{b|n}\left\{\sum_{d|(n/b)} f(d)g(b)\right\}$$

for every positive integer n. Argue that every term in the left-hand sum appears in the right-hand sum, and vice versa, by showing that if $d|n$ and $b|(n/d)$, then $b|n$ and $d|(n/b)$, and conversely.

3. Show that

$$\sum_{d|n}\frac{1}{d} = \frac{\sigma(n)}{n}$$

for every positive integer n.

6.3 Multiplicative Number-Theoretic Functions

The following theorems develop the basic properties of multiplicative number-theoretic functions.

Theorem 6.1. *If f is multiplicative and not identically zero, then $f(1) = 1$.*

PROOF. If f is not identically zero, then there must exist an integer n such that $f(n) \neq 0$. Since f is multiplicative and $(1, n) = 1$ for any n, it follows that

$$f(n) = f(1 \cdot n) = f(1)f(n).$$

Since $f(n) \neq 0$, we may divide both sides of this equation by $f(n)$ to obtain $f(1) = 1$ as desired.

Theorem 6.2. *Let $n = \Pi_{i=1}^{r} p_i^{n_i}$ be the canonical representation of the positive integer n. If f is multiplicative, then*

$$f(n) = \prod_{i=1}^{r} f(p_i^{n_i}).$$

PROOF. The proof is made by induction on r. If $r = 1$, the assertion is obviously true. Suppose that the assertion is true for $r = k$ and let $n = \Pi_{i=1}^{k+1} p_i^{n_i}$. By assumption,

$$f\left(\prod_{i=1}^{k} p_i^{n_i}\right) = \prod_{i=1}^{k} f(p_i^{n_i}).$$

Also, since

$$\left(\prod_{i=1}^{k} p_i^{n_i}, p_{k+1}^{n_{k+1}}\right) = 1$$

and f is multiplicative, it follows that

$$f(n) = f\left(\prod_{i=1}^{k} p_i^{n_i} \cdot p_{i+1}^{n_{k+1}}\right) = f\left(\prod_{i=1}^{k} p_i^{n_i}\right) \cdot f(p_{k+1}^{n_{k+1}}).$$

But then,

$$f(n) = \prod_{i=1}^{k+1} f(p_i^{n_i})$$

as desired.

The preceding theorem is particularly important since it reduces the problem of evaluating a number-theoretic function in general to the problem of evaluating it for prime powers, and this is usually much easier. For example, if one knew at the outset that $\sigma(n)$ was a multiplicative function, then this theorem would imply that

$$\sigma(n) = \prod_{i=1}^{r} \sigma(p_i^{n_i}).$$

But

$$\sigma(p_i^{n_i}) = \sum_{d \mid p_i^{n_i}} d$$

$$= 1 + p_i + p_i^2 + \cdots + p_i^{n_i} = \frac{p_i^{n_i+1} - 1}{p_i - 1}.$$

Hence, it follows that

$$\sigma(n) = \prod_{i=1}^{r} \frac{p_i^{n_i+1} - 1}{p_i - 1}$$

as before. Similarly, since $\tau(n)$ is multiplicative and $\tau(p_i^{n_i})$ is clearly equal to $n_i + 1$, we obtain

$$\tau(n) = \prod_{i=1}^{r} \tau(p_i^{n_i}) = \prod_{i=1}^{r} (n_i + 1).$$

Theorem 6.3. *If f and g are multiplicative, then so are $F = f \cdot g$ and $G = f/g$, whenever the latter function is defined.*

PROOF. Since f and g are multiplicative, we have that, for $(m, n) = 1$,

$$
\begin{aligned}
F(mn) &= f(mn)g(mn) \\
&= f(m)f(n)g(m)g(n) \\
&= f(m)g(m)f(n)g(n) \\
&= F(m)F(n).
\end{aligned}
$$

Thus, F is multiplicative. G is shown to be multiplicative in the same way.

Theorem 6.4. *If f and g are multiplicative, then so is $F(n) = \sum_{d|n} f(d)g(n/d)$.*

PROOF. If $(m, n) = 1$, then it follows immediately from consideration of the canonical representations of the numbers involved, that $d \mid mn$ if and only if $d = d_1 d_2$ where $d_1 \mid m$ and $d_2 \mid n$. It is clear that $(d_1, d_2) = 1 = (m/d_1, n/d_2)$. Therefore, since f and g are multiplicative, we have that

$$
\begin{aligned}
F(mn) &= \sum_{d|mn} f(d)g\left(\frac{mn}{d}\right) \\
&= \sum_{d_1|m} \sum_{d_2|n} f(d_1 d_2) g\left(\frac{mn}{d_1 d_2}\right) \\
&= \sum_{d_1|m} \sum_{d_2|n} f(d_1) f(d_2) g\left(\frac{m}{d_1}\right) g\left(\frac{n}{d_2}\right).
\end{aligned}
$$

But, by (6) in Section 6.2, as adapted from Chapter 1,

$$
\sum_{d_1|m} \sum_{d_2|n} f(d_1) f(d_2) g\left(\frac{m}{d_1}\right) g\left(\frac{n}{d_2}\right) = \sum_{d_1|m} f(d_1) g\left(\frac{m}{d_1}\right) \cdot \sum_{d_2|n} f(d_2) g\left(\frac{n}{d_2}\right)
$$

$$
= F(m)F(n).
$$

Therefore, $F(mn) = F(m)F(n)$ and F is multiplicative.

Corollary 6.5. *If f is multiplicative, then so is $F(n) = \sum_{d|n} f(d)$.*

PROOF. This follows immediately from the preceding theorem since the constant function $g(n) = 1$ for every n is clearly multiplicative.

Theorem 6.4 and Corollary 6.5 make it possible to construct new multiplicative functions from functions which are known to be multiplicative and frequently make it easy to show that functions are multiplicative. For example, since

$$
\tau(n) = \sum_{d|n} 1
$$

and the constant function $g(n) = 1$ is multiplicative, we easily deduce that $\tau(n)$ is multiplicative. Again, since

$$
\sigma(n) = \sum_{d|n} d
$$

and the function $f(n) = n$ is multiplicative, it follows that $\sigma(n)$ is multiplicative. Finally, suppose that we define $\sigma_\alpha(n) = \sum_{d|n} d^\alpha$. Since the function

$f(n) = n^\alpha$ is multiplicative, it follows from Corollary 6.5 that $\sigma_\alpha(n)$ is also multiplicative. Therefore, by Theorem 6.2,

$$\sigma_\alpha(n) = \prod_{i=1}^{r} \sigma_\alpha(p_i^{n_i})$$

if $n = \prod_{i=1}^{r} p_i^{n_i}$ is the canonical representation of n. But, for $\alpha \neq 0$,

$$\sigma_\alpha(p_i^{n_i}) = 1^\alpha + p_i^\alpha + p_i^{2\alpha} + \cdots + p_i^{n_i\alpha}$$

$$= \frac{p_i^{\alpha(n_i+1)} - 1}{p_i^\alpha - 1}.$$

Thus, it follows that

$$\sigma_\alpha(n) = \prod_{i=1}^{r} \frac{p_i^{\alpha(n_i+1)} - 1}{p_i^\alpha - 1}$$

and we have proved the following theorem.

Theorem 6.6 *If $\sigma_\alpha(n) = \sum_{d|n} d^\alpha$, $\alpha \neq 0$, and $n = \prod_{i=1}^{r} p_i^{n_i}$ is the canonical representation of n, then*

$$\sigma_\alpha(n) = \prod_{i=1}^{r} \frac{p_i^{\alpha(n_i+1)} - 1}{p_i^\alpha - 1}.$$

Exercises

1. If $n = \prod_{i=1}^{r} p_i^{n_i}$ is the canonical representation of n and f is completely multiplicative, show that $f(n) = \prod_{i=1}^{r} \{f(p_i)\}^{n_i}$.

2. Show that $\sigma_0(n) = \tau(n)$ and $\sigma_1(n) = \sigma(n)$.

3. Show that $\sigma_2(n) = \sigma(n) \cdot \prod_{i=1}^{r} \frac{p_i^{n_i+1} + 1}{p_i + 1}$ where $n = \prod_{i=1}^{r} p_i^{n_i}$ is the canonical representation of n.

4. For $n > 0$, show that

$$\sum_{d|n} \frac{1}{d^2} = \frac{\sigma_2(n)}{n^2}.$$

5. Let $p(n)$ denote the number of distinct prime divisors of n and let $q(n) = a^{p(n)}$. For $n > 0$, let $F(n) = \sum_{d|n} q(d)$ and find a formula for $F(n)$ in terms of a and the canonical representation of n.

6. For $n > 0$, let $\tau_2(n) = \sum_{d|n} \tau(d)$. Show that $\tau_2(n)$ is multiplicative and derive a formula for $\tau_2(n)$ in terms of the canonical representation of n.

7. Let $\tau_3(n) = \sum_{d|n} \tau_2(d)$ and derive a formula for $\tau_3(n)$ in terms of the canonical representation of n. *Hint:* You may need the result of Exercise 5, Section 1.2.

8. Let $\tau_k(n) = \sum_{d|n} \tau_{k-1}(d)$ for $k \geq 2$ where $\tau_1(n) = \tau(n)$. Derive a formula for $\tau_k(n)$ in terms of the canonical representation of n.

9. If $F(n) = \sum_{d|n} \tau^3(d)$, show that $F(n) = \tau_2^2(n)$.

6.4 Perfect Numbers

Mathematicians of every age have been fascinated by the special properties of various classes of numbers, and it is just this fascination which has produced the theory of numbers. In addition to the many examples already discussed which illustrate this point, we now consider the class of perfect numbers defined, in modern notation, as follows.

Definition 6.2. A positive integer a is called *perfect* in case $\sigma(a) = 2a$.

For example, since

$$\sigma(6) = 1 + 2 + 3 + 6 = 12$$

and

$$\sigma(28) = 1 + 2 + 4 + 7 + 14 + 28 = 56,$$

it follows that 6 and 28 are both *perfect*. Similarly, 496 and 8128 are perfect, and the reader may notice that each of these numbers is even. Indeed, the only known perfect numbers are even, and all of these are as characterized in the following theorem.

Theorem 6.7. *If $2^n - 1$ is a prime, then $a = 2^{n-1}(2^n - 1)$ is perfect and every even perfect number is of this form.*

PROOF. Let $a = 2^{n-1}(2^n - 1)$ where $2^n - 1$ is a prime. Then,

$$
\begin{aligned}
\sigma(a) &= \sigma[2^{n-1}(2^n - 1)] \\
&= \sigma(2^{n-1})\sigma(2^n - 1) \\
&= \frac{2^n - 1}{2 - 1} \cdot (2^n - 1 + 1) \\
&= 2^n(2^n - 1) \\
&= 2a,
\end{aligned}
$$

and it follows that a is perfect.

Conversely, suppose that a is an even perfect number. Determine n and m by the equation

$$a = m2^{n-1}$$

and the conditions $n \geq 2$, m odd, $m > 0$. Since a is perfect, we have that

$$
\begin{aligned}
m2^n &= 2a \\
&= \sigma(a) \\
&= \sigma(m2^{n-1}) \\
&= \sigma(m)\sigma(2^{n-1}) \\
&= \sigma(m)(2^n - 1).
\end{aligned}
$$

Therefore,

$$\sigma(m) = \frac{m2^n}{2^n - 1}.$$

Since $\sigma(m) = \dfrac{m2^n}{2^n - 1}$ is an integer and $(2^n, 2^n - 1) = 1$, this implies that

$(2^n - 1) \mid m$ and hence that $\dfrac{m}{2^n - 1} \Big| m$. Moreover,

$$\sigma(m) = \frac{m2^n}{2^n - 1} = m + \frac{m}{2^n - 1}$$

so that $\sigma(m)$ is equal to the sum of m and one other positive divisor of m. Thus, m must have *only* two positive divisors, and so must be a prime. Also, it must be the case that

$$\frac{m}{2^n - 1} = 1.$$

Therefore, $m = 2^n - 1$ and $a = 2^{n-1}(2^n - 1)$ where $2^n - 1$ is a prime.

Exercises

1. Is either 523,776 or 33,550,336 a perfect number? It may help to refer to the table of primes on pages 126–129.

2. If a is perfect, show that

$$\sum_{d \mid a} \frac{1}{d} = 2.$$

3. If a is perfect, show that

$$\sigma_2(a) = 2a \prod_{i=1}^{r} \frac{p_i^{a_i+1} + 1}{p_i + 1}$$

where $a = \prod_{i=1}^{r} p_i^{a_i}$ is the canonical representation of a.

6.5 The Möbius Inversion Formula

In Corollary 6.5, we considered the function F defined in terms of the function f by the equation

$$F(n) = \sum_{d \mid n} f(d)$$

for every positive integer n. Thus, we have

$$F(1) = f(1),$$
$$F(2) = f(1) + f(2),$$
$$F(3) = f(1) + f(3),$$
$$F(4) = f(1) + f(2) + f(4),$$
$$F(5) = f(1) + f(5),$$
$$F(6) = f(1) + f(2) + f(3) + f(6),$$

and so on. It is apparent that these equations can be solved successively for the values of f in terms of the values of F and we obtain

$$f(1) = F(1),$$
$$f(2) = F(2) - F(1),$$
$$f(3) = F(3) - F(1),$$
$$f(4) = F(4) - F(2),$$
$$f(5) = F(5) - F(1),$$
$$f(6) = F(6) - F(3) - F(2) + F(1).$$

Now, it is quite natural to ask how $f(n)$ can be expressed in terms of $F(1)$, $F(2), \ldots, F(n)$ for any value of n. Indeed, it is not difficult to guess from the preceding equations that the desired relationship is of the form

$$f(n) = \sum_{d \mid n} \mu(d) F\left(\frac{n}{d}\right),$$

where

$$\mu(1) = 1, \quad \mu(2) = -1, \quad \mu(3) = -1,$$
$$\mu(4) = 0, \quad \mu(5) = -1, \quad \mu(6) = 1.$$

The problem, of course, is to determine the nature of $\mu(n)$ for every n.

Since

$$F(p) = f(1) + f(p)$$

for any prime p, it is clear that

$$f(p) = F(p) - F(1)$$

and that $\mu(p)$ should have the value -1. Similarly, since

$$F(p^2) = f(1) + f(p) + f(p^2),$$

it follows that

$$f(p^2) = F(p^2) - [F(p) - F(1)] - F(1)$$
$$= F(p^2) - F(p)$$

so that $\mu(p^2)$ should equal 0. In the same way, we can conclude that $\mu(p^a)$ should equal 0 for every $a > 1$. If we further presume that μ is multiplicative, then it is clear that

$\mu(1) = 1,$
$\mu(n) = (-1)^r$ if $n = p_1 p_2 \cdots p_r$, where the p_i are distinct primes,
$\mu(n) = 0$ if $p^2 \mid n$ for any prime p.

Definition 6.3. The multiplicative number-theoretic function μ defined by the preceding equations is called the *Möbius function* after A. F. Möbius (1790–1868).

The following theorem shows that our guess concerning $\mu(n)$ and the relationship between the functions f and F above is correct.

Theorem 6.8 (The Möbius Inversion Formula). *If $f(n)$ is any number-theoretic function and $F(n) = \sum_{d|n} f(d)$ for $n \geq 1$, then*

$$f(n) = \sum_{d|n} \mu(d) F\left(\frac{n}{d}\right).$$

Before proving this theorem, it will be helpful to have the following result which depends on the fact that $\mu(n)$ is multiplicative.

Theorem 6.9. $\displaystyle\sum_{d|n} \mu(d) = 1$ *if $n = 1$,*

$$= 0 \ if \ n > 1.$$

PROOF. If $n = 1$, then

$$\sum_{d|n} \mu(d) = \sum_{d|1} \mu(d) = \mu(1) = 1.$$

For $n > 1$, let

$$M(n) = \sum_{d|n} \mu(d).$$

Since μ is multiplicative, it follows from Corollary 6.5 that $M(n)$ is multiplicative. Therefore, if $n = \Pi_{i=1}^{r} p_i^{n_i}$ is the canonical representation of n,

$$M(n) = \prod_{i=1}^{r} M(p_i^{n_i})$$

by Theorem 6.2. However, for each i,

$$M(p_i^{n_i}) = \sum_{d|p_i^{n_i}} \mu(d)$$

$$= \mu(1) + \mu(p_i) + \mu(p_i^2) + \cdots + \mu(p_i^{n_i})$$

$$= 1 + (-1) + 0 + \cdots + 0$$

$$= 0.$$

Thus, for $n > 1$, $\sum_{d|n} \mu(d) = M(n) = 0$ as claimed.

PROOF OF THEOREM 6.8. Suppose that $F(n) = \sum_{d|n} f(d)$. Then,

$$\sum_{d|n} \mu(d) F\left(\frac{n}{d}\right) = \sum_{d|n} \left\{ \mu(d) \cdot \sum_{b|(n/d)} f(b) \right\}$$

(9)

$$= \sum_{d|n} \left\{ \sum_{b|(n/d)} \mu(d) f(b) \right\}.$$

However, if $d \mid n$ and $b \mid (n/d)$, then n/d is an integer and $\dfrac{n/d}{b}$ is an integer. But

$$\frac{n/d}{b} = \frac{n}{bd} = \frac{n/b}{d}$$

and so n/b is an integer and $\dfrac{n/b}{d}$ is an integer. This says that $d \mid n$ and $b \mid (n/d)$ if and only if $b \mid n$ and $(d \mid n/b)$. Therefore, as in Exercise 2 of Section 6.2,

$$(10) \qquad \sum_{d \mid n} \left\{ \sum_{b \mid (n/d)} \mu(d)f(b) \right\} = \sum_{b \mid n} \left\{ \sum_{d \mid (n/b)} \mu(d)f(b) \right\}$$

since any term appearing in the left-hand sum must also appear in the right-hand sum, and vice versa. If we now combine (9) and (10), we obtain

$$\begin{aligned}
\sum_{d \mid n} \mu(d)F\left(\frac{n}{d}\right) &= \sum_{b \mid n} \left\{ \sum_{d \mid (n/b)} \mu(d)f(b) \right\} \\
&= \sum_{b \mid n} \left\{ f(b) \cdot \sum_{d \mid (n/b)} \mu(d) \right\} \\
&= f(n)
\end{aligned}$$

since, by Theorem 6.9, the inner sum in the last expression is equal to zero, except in the case $b = n$, when it equals 1.

6.6 The Euler ϕ-Function

The Euler ϕ-function, $\phi(n)$, which gives the number of positive integers less than or equal to n and relatively prime to n, was introduced in Section 4.4.

In this section, we prove that

$$\phi(n) = \prod_{i=1}^{r} p_i^{n_i - 1}(p_i - 1),$$

where $\Pi_{i=1}^{r} p_i^{n_i}$, with $n_i \geq 1$ for each i, is the canonical representation of n. The first theorem is the converse of Corollary 6.5.

Theorem 6.10. *If F is multiplicative and $F(n) = \sum_{d \mid n} f(d)$ for $n \geq 1$, then f is multiplicative.*

PROOF. Since $F(n) = \sum_{d \mid n} f(d)$, we have by the Möbius inversion formula that

$$f(n) = \sum_{d \mid n} \mu(d)F\left(\frac{n}{d}\right).$$

But then, by Theorem 6.4, f is multiplicative since μ and F are both multiplicative.

Theorem 6.11. *If n is a positive integer, then*

$$n = \sum_{d|n} \phi(d).$$

PROOF. Corresponding to each positive divisor d of n is a set of positive integers all less than or equal to n whose greatest common divisor with n is d. Moreover, each positive integer not exceeding n associates with one and only one d in this way. We shall, therefore, count each of the integers 1 through n precisely once if we count how many are associated with each d and take the sum over all values of d. For example, for $n = 12$, the following table lists the various possibilities for d and shows with which d each of the integers from 1 through 12 are associated.

Values of d	Associated Integers
1	1, 5, 7, 11
2	2, 10
3	3, 9
4	4, 8
6	6
12	12

In the general case, those integers which associate with a given d in the desired way are just those members of the set $d, 2d, \ldots, kd, \ldots, (n/d){\cdot}d$ for which $(kd, n) = d$; that is, those integers kd for which $(k, n/d) = 1$ and $k \leq n/d$. Of course, by definition of the ϕ-function, there are just $\phi(n/d)$ such values of k. Therefore, summing over all the positive divisors of n, we obtain

$$n = \sum_{d|n} \phi\left(\frac{n}{d}\right).$$

Finally, since

$$\sum_{d|n} \phi\left(\frac{n}{d}\right) = \sum_{d|n} \phi(d)$$

by (8) of Section 2, we obtain

$$n = \sum_{d|n} \phi(d).$$

Theorem 6.12. *ϕ is a multiplicative function.*

PROOF. As noted before, the function $F(n) = n$ is completely multiplicative. Therefore, since

$$F(n) = n = \sum_{d|n} \phi(d)$$

by Theorem 6.11, it follows from Theorem 6.10 that ϕ is multiplicative.

Theorem 6.13. *If n is a positive integer, then*

$$\phi(n) = n \sum_{d|n} \frac{\mu(d)}{d}.$$

PROOF. Applying the Möbius inversion formula to the formula

$$F(n) = n = \sum_{d|n} \phi(d),$$

we obtain

$$\phi(n) = \sum_{d|n} \mu(d) F\left(\frac{n}{d}\right)$$

$$= \sum_{d|n} \frac{n\mu(d)}{d} = n \sum_{d|n} \frac{\mu(d)}{d}.$$

Theorem 6.14. *If $n = \Pi_{i=1}^{r} p_i^{n_i}$ with $n_i \geq 1$ for each i, then*

$$\phi(n) = \prod_{i=1}^{r} p_i^{n_i-1}(p_i - 1).$$

PROOF. Since $\phi(n)$ is multiplicative, it follows from Theorem 6.2 that

$$\phi(n) = \prod_{i=1}^{r} \phi(p_i^{n_i}).$$

Also, by Theorem 6.13,

$$\phi(p_i^{n_i}) = p_i^{n_i} \cdot \sum_{d|p_i^{n_i}} \frac{\mu(d)}{d}$$

$$= p_i^{n_i} \cdot \left\{ \frac{\mu(1)}{1} + \frac{\mu(p_i)}{p_i} + \frac{\mu(p_i^2)}{p_i^2} + \cdots \right\} = p_i^{n_i} \cdot \left(1 - \frac{1}{p_i}\right)$$

since $\mu(p_i^a) = 0$ for $a \geq 2$. Therefore,

$$\phi(p_i^{n_i}) = p_i^{n_i-1}(p_i - 1)$$

for each i, and

$$\phi(n) = \prod_{i=1}^{r} \phi(p_i^{n_i}) = \prod_{i=1}^{r} p_i^{n_i-1}(p_i - 1).$$

An interesting and informative alternative proof of this theorem can be found in Chapter 5 of *Elementary Number Theory* by J. V. Uspensky and M. A. Heaslet (New York: McGraw-Hill Book Company, Inc., 1939).

As an example of the preceding theorem, we note that 1, 5, 7, and 11 are the four positive integers less than or equal to 12 and relatively prime to 12 and that $\phi(12) = \phi(2^2)\phi(3) = 2(2 - 1) \cdot 2 = 4$.

Exercises

1. For $n \geq 2$, prove that the sum of all a with $1 \leq a \leq n$ and $(a, n) = 1$, is $\phi(n) \cdot n/2$. *Hint:* Note that if $(a, n) = 1$, then $(n - a, n) = 1$.

2. Let $n = \prod_{i=1}^{r} p_i^{n_i}$ with $n_i \geq 1$ for each i. Let $f(n) = \sum_{d|n} \mu(d)\tau(d)$ and prove that $f(n) = (-1)^r$. *Hint:* Note that f is multiplicative since μ and τ are multiplicative and use Theorem 6.2.

3. If $g(n) = \sum_{d|n} \mu(d)\sigma(d)$, find a formula for $g(n)$ in terms of the canonical representation of n.

4. If $h(n) = \sum_{d|n} \mu(d)\phi(d)$, find a formula for $h(n)$ in terms of the canonical representation of n.

5. If f is a multiplicative number-theoretic function and $F(n) = \sum_{d|n} \mu(d)f(d)$ for every positive integer n, prove that $F(n) = \prod_{i=1}^{r} \{1 - f(p_i)\}$ if $n = \prod_{i=1}^{r} p_i^{n_i}$ with $n_i \geq 1$ for each i.

6. If $\alpha(n) = \sum_{d|n} \mu^2(d)/\phi(d)$ for every positive integer n, prove that $\alpha(n) = n/\phi(n)$.

7. If $n > 0$ and $\beta(n) = \sum_{d|n} \mu^2(d)/\tau(d)$, find a formula for $\beta(n)$ in terms of the canonical representation of n.

8. If $n > 0$ and $n^2 = \sum_{d|n} g(d)$, find a formula for $g(n)$ in terms of the canonical representation of n.

9. Let $f(1) = 1$ and $f(n) = (-1)^k$ for $n > 1$ where k is the total number of prime factors of n. For example, $f(2) = -1$, $f(6) = 1$, $f(9) = 1$, and $f(12) = -1$. Define $F(n)$ by $F(n) = \sum_{d|n} f(d)$ and prove that $F(n) = 1$ or $F(n) = 0$. For what values of n is $F(n) = 1$?

10. Prove that $\phi(mn) = d\phi(m)\phi(n)/\phi(d)$ for any positive integers m and n, with $d = (m, n)$.

6.7 Other Inversion Formulas

The French mathematician Henri Poincaré has said, "Suppose I apply myself to a complicated calculation and with much difficulty arrive at a result, I shall have gained nothing by my trouble if it has not enabled me to foresee the results of other analogous calculations, and to direct them with certainty, avoiding the blind groping with which I had to be content the first time." Thus, it is often worthwhile to give one's work a careful reappraisal to see if the methods employed might not be used to obtain similar, or, perhaps, more general, results. For example, careful consideration of the result

$$n = \sum_{d|n} \phi(d)$$

of Theorem 6.11 reveals that the left-hand side of the equality is the sum $\sum_{j=1}^{n} 1$, while the right-hand side is the sum over the positive divisors of n of the function $\phi(d)$ which may be defined by the summation

$$\phi(d) = \sum_{\substack{j=1 \\ (j,d)=1}}^{d} 1.$$

This suggests the possibility of proving the equality

$$s(n) = \sum_{d \mid n} g(d),$$

where the functions s and g are defined by the equations

$$s(n) = \sum_{j=1}^{n} f(j)$$

and

$$g(d) = \sum_{\substack{j=1 \\ (j,d)=1}}^{d} f(j),$$

and one would naturally try to use a method of proof similar to that of Theorem 6.11. Thus, let us associate each integer from 1 to n inclusive with a divisor d of n. As before, those integers associated with a given d are of the form kd with $1 \leq k \leq n/d$ and $(k, n/d) = 1$. The sum $\sum_{j=1}^{n} f(j)$ may then be obtained by summing over all values of d the sums associated with each d. That is,

$$\sum_{j=1}^{n} f(j) = \sum_{d \mid n} \sum_{\substack{k=1 \\ (k,n/d)=1}}^{n/d} f(kd)$$

$$= \sum_{d \mid n} s'\left(\frac{n}{d}\right),$$

where

$$s'\left(\frac{n}{d}\right) = \sum_{\substack{k=1 \\ (k,n/d)=1}}^{n/d} f(kd).$$

This is not quite what we expected, but it may be useful, and it does correspond rather well to the statement

$$n = \sum_{d \mid n} \phi\left(\frac{n}{d}\right)$$

which can be obtained from Theorem 6.11 by using equation (8) of Section 2. In any case, we have obtained the following theorem.

Theorem 6.15. *For any number-theoretic function f and any positive integer n,*

$$s(n) = \sum_{d \mid n} s'\left(\frac{n}{d}\right),$$

where

$$s(n) = \sum_{j=1}^{n} f(j) \quad \text{and} \quad s'\left(\frac{n}{d}\right) = \sum_{\substack{k=1 \\ (k,n/d)=1}}^{n/d} f(kd).$$

Corollary 6.16. *If f is completely multiplicative, then*

$$s(n) = f(n) \sum_{d|n} \frac{s^*(d)}{f(d)} \, ,$$

where

$$s(n) = \sum_{j=1}^{n} f(j) \quad and \quad s^*(n) = \sum_{\substack{k=1 \\ (k,n)=1}}^{n} f(k) \ for \ n > 0.$$

PROOF. Since f is completely multiplicative, $f(kd) = f(k)f(d)$. Therefore, in Theorem 6.15,

$$s'\!\left(\frac{n}{d}\right) = \sum_{\substack{k=1 \\ (k,n/d)=1}}^{n/d} f(k)f(d)$$

$$= f(d) \cdot \sum_{\substack{k=1 \\ (k,n/d)=1}}^{n/d} f(k)$$

$$= f(d)s^*\!\left(\frac{n}{d}\right)$$

and we obtain

(11)
$$s(n) = \sum_{d|n} f(d)s^*\!\left(\frac{n}{d}\right).$$

By (8) of Section 2, this can be rewritten in the form

(12)
$$s(n) = \sum_{d|n} f\!\left(\frac{n}{d}\right) s^*(d).$$

Now, let $qd = n$. Since f is completely multiplicative,

$$f(n) = f(qd) = f(q)f(d)$$

and it follows that

$$f\!\left(\frac{n}{d}\right) = f(q) = \frac{f(n)}{f(d)} \, .$$

Using this in (12), we obtain

$$s(n) = \sum_{d|n} \frac{f(n)s^*(d)}{f(d)}$$

$$= f(n) \sum_{d|n} \frac{s^*(d)}{f(d)}$$

as claimed.

The object of Theorem 6.11 was not so much to prove that $n = \sum_{d|n} \phi(d)$ as to obtain an equation which could be inverted by the Möbius inversion formula to obtain a formula for $\phi(n)$. Similarly, the object of the present sequence of theorems is to obtain a general formula for finding $s^*(n)$ in terms of the more easily found $s(n)$. To this end, we prove the following theorem.

Theorem 6.17. *If f is completely multiplicative and s and s* are as defined in Corollary 6.16, then*

$$s^*(n) = \sum_{d|n} \mu(d)f(d)s\left(\frac{n}{d}\right).$$

PROOF. As shown in the proof of Corollary 6.16, $f(n/d) = f(n)/f(d)$ if f is completely multiplicative and $d|n$. Using this result and applying the Möbius inversion formula to

$$\frac{s(n)}{f(n)} = \sum_{d|n} \frac{s^*(d)}{f(d)}$$

from Corollary 6.16, we obtain

$$\frac{s^*(n)}{f(n)} = \sum_{d|n} \mu(d) \frac{s(n/d)}{f(n/d)} = \frac{1}{f(n)} \sum_{d|n} \mu(d)f(d)s\left(\frac{n}{d}\right)$$

from which the desired result immediately follows.

As examples of the use of the preceding theorem, we prove as corollaries two results obtained earlier in the text by other means.

Corollary 6.18. *For any positive integer n,*

$$\phi(n) = n \sum_{d|n} \frac{\mu(d)}{d}.$$

PROOF. In Theorem 6.17, let $f(n) = 1$ for every n. Then f is completely multiplicative, $s^*(n) = \phi(n)$, $s(n/d) = n/d$, and the result follows immediately.

Corollary 6.19. *For $n \geq 2$, the sum of the positive integers not exceeding n and relatively prime to n is $\phi(n) \cdot n/2$.*

PROOF. In Theorem 6.17, let $f(n) = n$ for all n. Then $s^*(n)$ is the sum of the positive integers not exceeding n and relatively prime to n,

$$s\left(\frac{n}{d}\right) = \frac{\frac{n}{d}\left(\frac{n}{d}+1\right)}{2}$$

and

(13)
$$s^*(n) = \sum_{d|n} \mu(d) \cdot d \cdot \frac{\frac{n}{d}\left(\frac{n}{d}+1\right)}{2}$$

$$= \frac{n}{2} \cdot n \sum_{d|n} \frac{\mu(d)}{d} + \frac{n}{2} \sum_{d|n} \mu(d).$$

But, since $n \geq 2$, $\sum_{d|n} \mu(d) = 0$ by Theorem 6.9, and

$$n \sum_{d|n} \frac{\mu(d)}{d} = \phi(n)$$

by Theorem 6.13. Substituting these results in (13), we obtain

$$s^*(n) = \phi(n) \cdot n/2$$

as desired.

An interesting and instructive alternative proof of Theorem 6.17 can be obtained by making use of the result of Theorem 6.9 that

$$\sum_{d|n} \mu(d) = 1 \quad \text{for } n = 1,$$
$$= 0 \quad \text{for } n > 1.$$

The desired conclusion is a corollary to the following theorem.

Theorem 6.20. *If f is any number-theoretic function and n is a positive integer, then*

$$s^*(n) = \sum_{d|n} \mu(d) S\left(\frac{n}{d}\right),$$

where $S(n/d) = \sum_{j=1}^{n/d} f(dj)$ and s* is as defined in Corollary 6.16.

PROOF. By Theorem 6.9,

$$\sum_{d|(k,n)} \mu(d) = 1 \quad \text{if } (k, n) = 1,$$
$$= 0 \quad \text{if } (k, n) > 1.$$

Therefore,

$$s^*(n) = \sum_{\substack{k=1 \\ (k,n)=1}}^{n} f(k)$$

(14)
$$= \sum_{k=1}^{n} \left\{ f(k) \cdot \sum_{d|(k,n)} \mu(d) \right\}$$

$$= \sum_{k=1}^{n} \sum_{d|(k,n)} f(k)\mu(d).$$

But, $1 \le k \le n$ and $d \mid (n, k)$ if and only if $d|n$, $k = jd$, and $1 \le j \le n/d$. Therefore,

(15)
$$\sum_{k=1}^{n} \sum_{d|(k,n)} f(k)\mu(d) = \sum_{d|n} \sum_{j=1}^{n/d} f(jd)\mu(d),$$

since each term in the left-hand sum appears in the right-hand sum, and vice versa. Combining (14) and (15), we obtain

$$s^*(n) = \sum_{d|n} \sum_{j=1}^{n/d} f(jd)\mu(d)$$

$$= \sum_{d|n} \left\{ \mu(d) \sum_{j=1}^{n/d} f(jd) \right\}$$

$$= \sum_{d|n} \mu(d) S\left(\frac{n}{d}\right).$$

ALTERNATIVE PROOF OF THEOREM 6.17. Suppose that f is completely multiplicative. Then, in Theorem 6.20,

$$S\left(\frac{n}{d}\right) = \sum_{j=1}^{n/d} f(jd)$$

$$= \sum_{j=1}^{n/d} f(j)f(d)$$

$$= f(d) \sum_{j=1}^{n/d} f(j)$$

$$= f(d)s\left(\frac{n}{d}\right),$$

where s is as in Theorem 6.17. Thus, from Theorem 6.20, we obtain

$$s^*(n) = \sum_{d \mid n} \mu(d)f(d)s\left(\frac{n}{d}\right)$$

as required.

Exercises

1. Prove that

$$\sum_{\substack{k=1 \\ (k,n)=1}}^{n} k^2 = \frac{n^2\phi(n)}{3} + \frac{n}{6} \prod_{i=1}^{r} (1 - p_i)$$

if $n > 1$ and $n = \prod_{i=1}^{r} p_i^{n_i}$ is the canonical representation of n. *Hint:* Use Exercise 5, Section 6 to conclude that

$$\sum_{d \mid n} d\mu(d) = \prod_{i=1}^{r} (1 - p_i).$$

2. Prove that

$$\sum_{\substack{k=1 \\ (k,n)=1}}^{n} k^3 = \frac{n^3\phi(n)}{4} + \frac{n^2}{4} \prod_{i=1}^{r} (1 - p_i)$$

if $n > 1$ and $n = \prod_{i=1}^{r} p_i^{n_i}$ is the canonical representation of n.

6.8 The Greatest Integer Function

The greatest integer function, introduced in Definition 5.3, page 85, is frequently quite useful in treating number-theoretic problems. In this section, we develop the principal properties of the function and show some interesting applications. The reader should note that we continue to use small Latin letters to represent integers.

Theorem 6.21. *In the following, α, β, and θ denote real numbers.*

(a) $\alpha - 1 < [\alpha] \leq \alpha$.

(b) *If $a \leq \alpha$, then $a \leq [\alpha]$.*

(c) *If $a > \alpha$, then $a \geq [\alpha] + 1 > [\alpha]$.*

(d) *If $\alpha \leq \beta$, then $[\alpha] \leq [\beta]$.*

(e) *If $\theta = \alpha - [\alpha]$, then $0 \leq \theta < 1$.*

(f) *If $\alpha = n + \theta$ with $0 \leq \theta < 1$, then $n = [\alpha]$.*

(g) *For any integer n, $[\alpha + n] = [\alpha] + n$.*

(h) *If $a = bq + r$ with $0 \leq r < b$, then $q = [a/b]$.*

PROOF.

(a) The inequality $\alpha - 1 < [\alpha] \leq \alpha$ is simply a restatement of the defining inequality for $[\alpha]$.

(b) If $a + 1 > \alpha$, then $a \leq \alpha < a + 1$ and $a = [\alpha]$ by Definition 5.3. If $a + 1 \not> \alpha$, then $a + 1 \leq \alpha$ and $a \leq \alpha - 1 < [\alpha]$, by Part (a) above.

(c) By definition, $[\alpha] \leq \alpha$. Since $a > \alpha$, it follows that $a > [\alpha]$. Thus, $a \geq [\alpha] + 1$ since a and $[\alpha]$ are both integers.

(d) By definition, $[\alpha] \leq \alpha$. Therefore, since $\alpha \leq \beta$, it follows that $[\alpha] \leq \beta$. But $[\alpha]$ is an integer and so, by Part (b), $[\alpha] \leq [\beta]$.

(e) The inequality $0 \leq \alpha - [\alpha] < 1$ follows immediately from Part (a). Thus, $0 \leq \theta < 1$, since $\theta = \alpha - [\alpha]$.

(f) Since $0 \leq \theta < 1$ and $\alpha = n + \theta$, it follows that $n \leq \alpha < n + 1$. But then $n = [\alpha]$ by Definition 5.3.

(g) By Part (e), $\alpha = [\alpha] + \theta$ with $0 \leq \theta < 1$. Therefore, $\alpha + n = [\alpha] + n + \theta$ and $[\alpha + n] = [\alpha] + n$ by Part (f).

(h) Since $a = bq + r$ with $0 \leq r < b$, it follows that

$$\frac{a}{b} = q + \frac{r}{b}$$

with $0 \leq r/b < 1$. Therefore, by Part (f), $q = [a/b]$.

Theorem 6.22. *For any real number α and any integer $n > 0$,*

$$\left[\frac{[\alpha]}{n}\right] = \left[\frac{\alpha}{n}\right].$$

PROOF. By definition,

$$\left[\frac{\alpha}{n}\right] \leq \frac{\alpha}{n} < \left[\frac{\alpha}{n}\right] + 1.$$

Therefore,

$$n \cdot \left[\frac{\alpha}{n}\right] \leq \alpha < n \cdot \left[\frac{\alpha}{n}\right] + n,$$

and it follows from Parts (b) and (c) of the preceding theorem that

$$n \cdot \left[\frac{\alpha}{n}\right] \leq [\alpha] < n \cdot \left[\frac{\alpha}{n}\right] + n.$$

But this implies that

$$\left[\frac{\alpha}{n}\right] \leq \frac{[\alpha]}{n} < \left[\frac{\alpha}{n}\right] + 1,$$

and so

$$\left[\frac{\alpha}{n}\right] = \left[\frac{[\alpha]}{n}\right]$$

by Definition 5.3, since $[\alpha/n]$ is an integer.

Theorem 6.23. *If n is a positive integer and p is a prime, then p appears in the canonical representation of $n!$ with the exponent*

$$e = \left[\frac{n}{p}\right] + \left[\frac{n}{p^2}\right] + \cdots + \left[\frac{n}{p^r}\right],$$

where r is determined by the inequality $p^r \leq n < p^{r+1}$.

PROOF. For a given integer k, the multiples of p^k which do not exceed n are $p^k, 2p^k, \ldots, qp^k$ where q is the largest integer such that $qp^k \leq n$. But this says that q is the largest integer not exceeding n/p^k; so that $q = [n/p^k]$. Thus, $[n/p^k]$ gives the number of positive multiples of p^k which do not exceed n. Now, if $1 \leq m \leq n$, then $m = qp^k$ with $(q, p) = 1$, $0 \leq k \leq r$, and m contributes precisely k to the total exponent e with which p appears in the canonical representation of $n!$. Moreover, m is counted precisely k times by the sum

$$\left[\frac{n}{p}\right] + \left[\frac{n}{p^2}\right] + \cdots + \left[\frac{n}{p^r}\right],$$

once as a multiple of p, once as a multiple of $p^2, \ldots$, once as a multiple of p^k, and no more. Of course, if $k = 0$, then m is not counted in the sum. Therefore, the above sum accounts exactly for the contribution of each m between 1 and n to the exponent e as claimed.

As an example of the preceding theorem, consider the case for $n = 28$, $p = 3$. For $0 \leq k \leq 3$, let S_k denote the set of integers m with $1 \leq m \leq 28$ of the form $m = q \cdot 3^k$, $(q, 3) = 1$. Thus,

$$S_0 = \{1, 2, 4, 5, 7, 8, 10, 11, 13, 14, 16, 17, 19, 20, 22, 23, 25, 26, 28\},$$
$$S_1 = \{3, 6, 12, 15, 21, 24\},$$
$$S_2 = \{9, 18\},$$
$$S_3 = \{27\}.$$

Clearly, each element of S_0 contributes nothing to the exponent e with which 3 appears in the canonical representation of 28!. Each element of S_1 contributes 1 to e, each element of S_2 contributes 2, and each element of S_3 contributes 3. Thus, in this case,

$$e = 6 + 4 + 3 = 13.$$

Moreover, $[28/3] = 9$, the number of elements in S_1, S_2, and S_3; $[28/9] = 3$, the number of elements in S_2 and S_3; $[28/27] = 1$, the number of elements in S_3; and

$$9 + 3 + 1 = 13 = e.$$

Now, by Theorem 6.22,
$$\left[\frac{n}{p^2}\right] = \left[\frac{[n/p]}{p}\right],$$
$$\left[\frac{n}{p^3}\right] = \left[\frac{[n/p^2]}{p}\right],$$
. . . .

Also, by Part (h) of Theorem 6.21, $[n/p]$ is the quotient obtained when n is divided by p, $\left[\dfrac{[n/p]}{p}\right]$ is the quotient obtained when $[n/p]$ is divided by p, and so on. Thus, the work of determining the exponent of p in the canonical representation of $n!$ can be conveniently arranged as a sequence of divisions by p, the sum of the successive quotients yielding the desired exponent. For example, for $p = 3$ and $n = 28$, one would have

$$
\begin{array}{r|l}
3 & 28 \\ \hline
3 & 9 \\ \hline
3 & 3 \\ \hline
3 & 1 \\ \hline
 & 0
\end{array}
$$

where 28 is divided by 3, and then each successive quotient (ignoring remainders) is divided by 3 until a quotient of 0 is obtained. Thus, $[28/3] = 9$, $[28/3^2] = 3$, $[28/3^3] = 1$, and the desired exponent is 13, as before.

The preceding computation of the exponent of 3 in the canonical representation of 28! bears a marked resemblance to the calculation of the digits in the positional representation of 28 to base 3. That this resemblance is more than superficial is shown by the following theorem.

Theorem 6.24. *If p is a prime, if*
$$n = a_0 + a_1 p + a_2 p^2 + \cdots + a_r p^r$$
with $a_r \neq 0$ and $0 \leq a_i < p$ for each i, and if e is the exponent of p in the canonical representation of $n!$; then
$$e = \frac{n - (a_0 + a_1 + \cdots + a_r)}{p - 1}.$$

PROOF. Since
$$n = a_0 + a_1 p + \cdots + a_r p^r$$
with $a_r \neq 0$ and $0 \leq a_i < p$ for each i, it is clear that
$$\left[\frac{n}{p}\right] = a_1 + a_2 p + \cdots + a_r p^{r-1},$$
$$\left[\frac{n}{p^2}\right] = a_2 + a_3 p + \cdots + a_r p^{r-2},$$
. . . . ,
$$\left[\frac{n}{p^r}\right] = a_r.$$

From these equations, it readily follows that

$$a_0 + p\left[\frac{n}{p}\right] = n,$$

$$a_1 + p\left[\frac{n}{p^2}\right] = \left[\frac{n}{p}\right],$$

$$a_2 + p\left[\frac{n}{p^3}\right] = \left[\frac{n}{p^2}\right],$$

$$\cdots\cdots\cdots\cdots,$$

$$a_{r-1} + p\left[\frac{n}{p^r}\right] = \left[\frac{n}{p^{r-1}}\right],$$

$$a_r = \left[\frac{n}{p^r}\right].$$

If we now add these equations and make use of the fact that

$$e = \left[\frac{n}{p}\right] + \left[\frac{n}{p^2}\right] + \cdots + \left[\frac{n}{p^r}\right],$$

we obtain

$$(a_0 + a_1 + \cdots + a_r) + pe = n + e,$$

from which the desired result immediately follows.

Note that $28_{10} = 1001_3$. Therefore, using the formula of the preceding theorem, we again obtain

$$e = \frac{28 - (1 + 0 + 0 + 1)}{3 - 1} = 13$$

as the exponent of 3 in the canonical representation of 28!

Exercises

1. Evaluate the following:
   (a) $[2.7]$ (b) $[-3.5]$ (c) $[-\sqrt{2}]$ (d) $[75/4]$
   (e) $-[-2.7]$ (f) $-[3.5]$ (g) $-[\sqrt{2}]$ (h) $-[-75/4]$
   (i) $[2.7 + 0.5]$ (j) $[-3.5 + 0.5]$ (k) $[-\sqrt{2} + 0.5]$ (l) $[75/4 + 1/2]$
2. (a) Under what conditions is $[\alpha] + [\alpha] = [2\alpha]$?
   (b) Under what conditions is $[\alpha] + [-\alpha] \neq 0$?
3. Prove that $-[-\alpha]$ is the least integer not less than α.
4. Prove that no integer is nearer α than $[\alpha + \frac{1}{2}]$. If two integers are equally near, show that $[\alpha + \frac{1}{2}]$ is the larger of the two integers.
5. Prove that no integer is nearer α than $-[-\alpha + \frac{1}{2}]$. If two integers are equally near α, show that $-[-\alpha + \frac{1}{2}]$ is the smaller of the two integers.
6. Prove that $[\alpha] + [\alpha + \frac{1}{2}] = [2\alpha]$ for every real number α. *Hint:* $\alpha = [\alpha] + \theta$ with $0 \leq \theta < 1$. Consider two cases: $0 \leq \theta < \frac{1}{2}$ and $\frac{1}{2} \leq \theta < 1$.
7. Prove that $[\alpha] + [\alpha + \frac{1}{3}] + [\alpha + \frac{2}{3}] = [3\alpha]$ for every real number α.

8. Prove that

$$[\alpha] + \left[\alpha + \frac{1}{k}\right] + \left[\alpha + \frac{2}{k}\right] + \cdots + \left[\alpha + \frac{k-1}{k}\right] = [k\alpha]$$

for every real number α and any integer $k \geq 1$. *Hint:* $\alpha = [\alpha] + \theta$ with $0 \leq \theta < 1$. Consider $[k\theta] \leq k\theta < [k\theta] + 1$.

9. Find the exponent of 3 in the canonical representation of 91!

10. Show that 3 does not divide the binomial coefficient $\binom{91}{10}$.

11. Find the highest power of 10 which divides 91!

12. If α and β are real numbers, prove that

$$[\alpha] + [\beta] \leq [\alpha + \beta].$$

Hint: Use Part (d) of Theorem 6.21.

13. Use the result of the preceding exercise to prove that

$$\frac{(a + b)!}{a! b!}$$

is an integer for any positive integers a and b.

14. If n is a positive integer and α is real and not an integer, prove that

$$\left[\frac{[\alpha]}{-n}\right] = \left[\frac{\alpha}{-n}\right] \qquad \text{if } n \nmid [\alpha],$$

$$= \left[\frac{\alpha}{-n}\right] + 1 \quad \text{if } n \mid [\alpha].$$

6.9 A Further Inversion Formula

Careful consideration of the statement and proof of Theorem 6.20 reveals that the same method of proof can be used to obtain the following more general result involving the greatest integer function.

Theorem 6.25. *Let*

$$s^*(m, n) = \sum_{\substack{k=1 \\ (k,n)=1}}^{m} f(k)$$

where f is any number-theoretic function. *Then*

$$s^*(m, n) = \sum_{d \mid n} \left\{ \mu(d) \cdot \sum_{j=1}^{[m/d]} f(dj) \right\}.$$

Of course, if $m = n$, this reduces to the statement of Theorem 6.20.

PROOF. As in the proof of Theorem 6.20,

$$s^*(m, n) = \sum_{k=1}^{m} \left\{ f(k) \cdot \sum_{d|(k,n)} \mu(d) \right\}$$

$$= \sum_{k=1}^{m} \sum_{d|(k,n)} f(k)\mu(d)$$

$$= \sum_{d|n} \sum_{j=1}^{[m/d]} f(dj)\mu(d)$$

$$= \sum_{d|n} \left\{ \mu(d) \cdot \sum_{j=1}^{[m/d]} f(dj) \right\}.$$

Corollary 6.26. *Let $\phi(m, n)$ denote the number of positive integers not exceeding m which are relatively prime to n. Then*

$$\phi(m, n) = \sum_{d|n} \mu(d) \left[\frac{m}{d} \right].$$

PROOF. In Theorem 6.25, take $f(n) = 1$ for every n. Then $s^*(m, n) = \phi(m, n)$,

$$\sum_{j=1}^{[m/d]} f(dj) = \sum_{j=1}^{[m/d]} 1 = \left[\frac{m}{d} \right],$$

and it immediately follows that

$$\phi(m, n) = \sum_{d|n} \mu(d) \left[\frac{m}{d} \right].$$

Theorem 6.27. *As usual, let $\pi(m)$ denote the number of primes not exceeding the positive integer m. If p_i denotes the ith prime, $p_r \leq \sqrt{m} < p_{r+1}$, and $n = \Pi_{i=1}^{r} p_i$; then*

$$\pi(m) = \pi(\sqrt{m}) - 1 + \sum_{d|n} \mu(d) \left[\frac{m}{d} \right].$$

PROOF. By Corollary 6.26,

$$\phi(m, n) = \sum_{d|n} \mu(d) \left[\frac{m}{d} \right]$$

gives the number of positive integers not exceeding m which are relatively prime to n. But, since n is the product of all of the primes not exceeding $\sqrt{m}$, those integers not exceeding m and relatively prime to n are the integer 1 and the primes greater than $\sqrt{m}$ and less than or equal to m. Thus,

$$\pi(m) - \pi(\sqrt{m}) + 1 = \sum_{d|n} \mu(d) \left[\frac{m}{d} \right],$$

and the result follows immediately.

Exercises

1. If m and n are positive integers, let $g(m, n)$ denote the sum of the positive integers not exceeding m and relatively prime to n. Show that

$$g(m, n) = \sum_{d|n} d\mu(d) \left[\frac{m}{d}\right]\left[\frac{m}{d} + 1\right] / 2.$$

2. Use the result of Theorem 6.27 to find $\pi(168)$.

3. If f is completely multiplicative and $k > 0$, prove that

$$s^*(kn, n) = \sum_{d|n} \mu(d)f(d)s\left(\frac{kn}{d}\right),$$

where s *and* s^* are as defined in Corollary 6.16.

4. For $k > 0$, $n > 0$, prove that $\phi(kn, n) = k \cdot \phi(n)$.

5. For $k > 0$, $n > 1$, prove that

$$\sum_{\substack{h=1 \\ (h,n)=1}}^{kn} h = k^2\phi(n) \cdot \frac{n}{2}.$$

6. For $k > 0$, $n > 1$, prove that

$$\sum_{\substack{h=1 \\ (h,n)=1}}^{kn} h^2 = \frac{k^3 n^2 \phi(n)}{3} + \frac{kn}{6} \prod_{i=1}^{r} (1 - p_i),$$

where $n = \prod_{i=1}^{r} p_i^{n_i}$, with $n_i \geq 1$ for each i, is the canonical representation of n.

References

1. Davenport, H., *The Higher Arithmetic*. London: Hutchinson's University Library, 1952 (distributed by Hillary House Publishers Ltd., New York). Also available as a Harper Torchbook (New York: Harper & Row, Publishers, Inc., 1960).

2. Dickson, L. E., *History of the Theory of Numbers*, 3 vols. Washington: Carnegie Institution of Washington, 1919–1923. New York: Chelsea Publishing Company, 1952.

3. Dickson, L. E., *Modern Elementary Theory of Numbers*. Chicago: The University of Chicago Press, 1939.

4. Hardy, G. H., and Wright, E. M., *An Introduction to the Theory of Numbers*, 4th edition. New York: Oxford University Press, 1960.

5. Lehmer, D. H., *Guide to Tables in the Theory of Numbers*. Washington: Bulletin of the National Research Council, No. 105, 1941.

6. LeVeque, W. J., *Elementary Theory of Numbers*. Reading, Massachusetts: Addison-Wesley Publishing Company, Inc., 1962.

7. Nagell, T., *Introduction to Number Theory*. New York: John Wiley & Sons, Inc., 1951.

8. Niven, I., and Zuckerman, H. S., *An Introduction to the Theory of Numbers*. New York: John Wiley & Sons, Inc., 1960.

9. Ore, O., *Number Theory and its History*. New York: McGraw-Hill Book Company, Inc., 1948.

10. Stewart, B. M., *Theory of Numbers*, 2d edition. New York: The Macmillan Company, 1964.

11. Uspensky, J. V., and Heaslet, M. H., *Elementary Number Theory*. New York: McGraw-Hill Book Company, Inc., 1939.

12. Vinogradov, I. M., *Elements of Number Theory*, translated from the fifth Russian edition by Saul Kravetz. New York: Dover Publications, Inc., 1954.

Table of Prime Numbers Less Than Ten Thousand

2	151	353	577	811	1049	1297	1559
3	157	359	587	821	1051	1301	1567
5	163	367	593	823	1061	1303	1571
7	167	373	599	827	1063	1307	1579
11	173	379	601	829	1069	1319	1583
13	179	383	607	839	1087	1321	1597
17	181	389	613	853	1091	1327	1601
19	191	397	617	857	1093	1361	1607
23	193	401	619	859	1097	1367	1609
29	197	409	631	863	1103	1373	1613
31	199	419	641	877	1109	1381	1619
37	211	421	643	881	1117	1399	1621
41	223	431	647	883	1123	1409	1627
43	227	433	653	887	1129	1423	1637
47	229	439	659	907	1151	1427	1657
53	233	443	661	911	1153	1429	1663
59	239	449	673	919	1163	1433	1667
61	241	457	677	929	1171	1439	1669
67	251	461	683	937	1181	1447	1693
71	257	463	691	941	1187	1451	1697
73	263	467	701	947	1193	1453	1699
79	269	479	709	953	1201	1459	1709
83	271	487	719	967	1213	1471	1721
89	277	491	727	971	1217	1481	1723
97	281	499	733	977	1223	1483	1733
101	283	503	739	983	1229	1487	1741
103	293	509	743	991	1231	1489	1747
107	307	521	751	997	1237	1493	1753
109	311	523	757	1009	1249	1499	1759
113	313	541	761	1013	1259	1511	1777
127	317	547	769	1019	1277	1523	1783
131	331	557	773	1021	1279	1531	1787
137	337	563	787	1031	1283	1543	1789
139	347	569	797	1033	1289	1549	1801
149	349	571	809	1039	1291	1553	1811

1823	2131	2437	2749	3083	3433	3733	4073
1831	2137	2441	2753	3089	3449	3739	4079
1847	2141	2447	2767	3109	3457	3761	4091
1861	2143	2459	2777	3119	3461	3767	4093
1867	2153	2467	2789	3121	3463	3769	4099
1871	2161	2473	2791	3137	3467	3779	4111
1873	2179	2477	2797	3163	3469	3793	4127
1877	2203	2503	2801	3167	3491	3797	4129
1879	2207	2521	2803	3169	3499	3803	4133
1889	2213	2531	2819	3181	3511	3821	4139
1901	2221	2539	2833	3187	3517	3823	4153
1907	2237	2543	2837	3191	3527	3833	4157
1913	2239	2549	2843	3203	3529	3847	4159
1931	2243	2551	2851	3209	3533	3851	4177
1933	2251	2557	2857	3217	3539	3853	4201
1949	2267	2579	2861	3221	3541	3863	4211
1951	2269	2591	2879	3229	3547	3877	4217
1973	2273	2593	2887	3251	3557	3881	4219
1979	2281	2609	2897	3253	3559	3889	4229
1987	2287	2617	2903	3257	3571	3907	4231
1993	2293	2621	2909	3259	3581	3911	4241
1997	2297	2633	2917	3271	3583	3917	4243
1999	2309	2647	2927	3299	3593	3919	4253
2003	2311	2657	2939	3301	3607	3923	4259
2011	2333	2659	2953	3307	3613	3929	4261
2017	2339	2663	2957	3313	3617	3931	4271
2027	2341	2671	2963	3319	3623	3943	4273
2029	2347	2677	2969	3323	3631	3947	4283
2039	2351	2683	2971	3329	3637	3967	4289
2053	2357	2687	2999	3331	3643	3989	4297
2063	2371	2689	3001	3343	3659	4001	4327
2069	2377	2693	3011	3347	3671	4003	4337
2081	2381	2699	3019	3359	3673	4007	4339
2083	2383	2707	3023	3361	3677	4013	4349
2087	2389	2711	3037	3371	3691	4019	4357
2089	2393	2713	3041	3373	3697	4021	4363
2099	2399	2719	3049	3389	3701	4027	4373
2111	2411	2729	3061	3391	3709	4049	4391
2113	2417	2731	3067	3407	3719	4051	4397
2129	2423	2741	3079	3413	3727	4057	4409

4421	4759	5099	5449	5801	6143	6481	6841
4423	4783	5101	5471	5807	6151	6491	6857
4441	4787	5107	5477	5813	6163	6521	6863
4447	4789	5113	5479	5821	6173	6529	6869
4451	4793	5119	5483	5827	6197	6547	6871
4457	4799	5147	5501	5839	6199	6551	6883
4463	4801	5153	5503	5843	6203	6553	6899
4481	4813	5167	5507	5849	6211	6563	6907
4483	4817	5171	5519	5851	6217	6569	6911
4493	4831	5179	5521	5857	6221	6571	6917
4507	4861	5189	5527	5861	6229	6577	6947
4513	4871	5197	5531	5867	6247	6581	6949
4517	4877	5209	5557	5869	6257	6599	6959
4519	4889	5227	5563	5879	6263	6607	6961
4523	4903	5231	5569	5881	6269	6619	6967
4547	4909	5233	5573	5897	6271	6637	6971
4549	4919	5237	5581	5903	6277	6653	6977
4561	4931	5261	5591	5923	6287	6659	6983
4567	4933	5273	5623	5927	6299	6661	6991
4583	4937	5279	5639	5939	6301	6673	6997
4591	4943	5281	5641	5953	6311	6679	7001
4597	4951	5297	5647	5981	6317	6689	7013
4603	4957	5303	5651	5987	6323	6691	7019
4621	4967	5309	5653	6007	6329	6701	7027
4637	4969	5323	5657	6011	6337	6703	7039
4639	4973	5333	5659	6029	6343	6709	7043
4643	4987	5347	5669	6037	6353	6719	7057
4649	4993	5351	5683	6043	6359	6733	7069
4651	4999	5381	5689	6047	6361	6737	7079
4657	5003	5387	5693	6053	6367	6761	7103
4663	5009	5393	5701	6067	6373	6763	7109
4673	5011	5399	5711	6073	6379	6779	7121
4679	5021	5407	5717	6079	6389	6781	7127
4691	5023	5413	5737	6089	6397	6791	7129
4703	5039	5417	5741	6091	6421	6793	7151
4721	5051	5419	5743	6101	6427	6803	7159
4723	5059	5431	5749	6113	6449	6823	7177
4729	5077	5437	5779	6121	6451	6827	7187
4733	5081	5441	5783	6131	6469	6829	7193
4751	5087	5443	5791	6133	6473	6833	7207

7211	7561	7907	8273	8647	8971	9337	9677
7213	7573	7919	8287	8663	8999	9341	9679
7219	7577	7927	8291	8669	9001	9343	9689
7229	7583	7933	8293	8677	9007	9349	9697
7237	7589	7937	8297	8681	9011	9371	9719
7243	7591	7949	8311	8689	9013	9377	9721
7247	7603	7951	8317	8693	9029	9391	9733
7253	7607	7963	8329	8699	9041	9397	9739
7283	7621	7993	8353	8707	9043	9403	9743
7297	7639	8009	8363	8713	9049	9413	9749
7307	7643	8011	8369	8719	9059	9419	9767
7309	7649	8017	8377	8731	9067	9421	9769
7321	7669	8039	8387	8737	9091	9431	9781
7331	7673	8053	8389	8741	9103	9433	9787
7333	7681	8059	8419	8747	9109	9437	9791
7349	7687	8069	8423	8753	9127	9439	9803
7351	7691	8081	8429	8761	9133	9461	9811
7369	7699	8087	8431	8779	9137	9463	9817
7393	7703	8089	8443	8783	9151	9467	9829
7411	7717	8093	8447	8803	9157	9473	9833
7417	7723	8101	8461	8807	9161	9479	9839
7433	7727	8111	8467	8819	9173	9491	9851
7451	7741	8117	8501	8821	9181	9497	9857
7457	7753	8123	8513	8831	9187	9511	9859
7459	7757	8147	8521	8837	9199	9521	9871
7477	7759	8161	8527	8839	9203	9533	9883
7481	7789	8167	8537	8849	9209	9539	9887
7487	7793	8171	8539	8861	9221	9547	9901
7489	7817	8179	8543	8863	9227	9551	9907
7499	7823	8191	8563	8867	9239	9587	9923
7507	7829	8209	8573	8887	9241	9601	9929
7517	7841	8219	8581	8893	9257	9613	9931
7523	7853	8221	8597	8923	9277	9619	9941
7529	7867	8231	8599	8929	9281	9623	9949
7537	7873	8233	8609	8933	9283	9629	9967
7541	7877	8237	8623	8941	9293	9631	9973
7547	7879	8243	8627	8951	9311	9643	
7549	7883	8263	8629	8963	9319	9649	
7559	7901	8269	8641	8969	9323	9661	

Answers to
Selected Exercises

Section 1.2

1. (c) $\dfrac{2}{1 \cdot 2} + \dfrac{2}{2 \cdot 3} + \cdots + \dfrac{2}{n(n+1)}$

2. (c) $\sum_{k=1}^{6} (25 + 3k)$

3. Since $a_0 = 0$, $\sum_{i=1}^{n} (a_i - a_{i-1}) = a_n$.

4. Set $a_n = n(n+1)/2$. Then $a_0 = 0$ and

$$a_i - a_{i-1} = \frac{i(i+1)}{2} - \frac{(i-1)i}{2} = i.$$

Therefore, using the result of Exercise 3, we have

$$\sum_{i=1}^{n} i = \sum_{i=1}^{n} (a_i - a_{i-1}) = a_n = \frac{n(n+1)}{2}.$$

6. Note that $i^2 = i(i+1) - i$. Thus, it follows from Exercises 4 and 5 that

$$\sum_{i=1}^{n} i^2 = \frac{n(n+1)(n+2)}{3} - \frac{n(n+1)}{2} = \frac{n(n+1)(2n+1)}{6}.$$

7. (c) $p(p+1) \cdots (p+n) = \dfrac{(p+n)!}{(p-1)!}$

8. (b) $\prod_{i=1}^{n} (-i)$

10. Since $a_0 = 1$, $\displaystyle\prod_{i=1}^{n} \frac{a_i}{a_{i-1}} = a_n$.

Section 1.4

1. For $n = 1$, the assertion of the problem is that

$$\frac{1}{1(1+1)} = \frac{1}{1+1}$$

and this is clearly true. Now suppose that

$$\sum_{i=1}^{k} \frac{1}{i(i+1)} = \frac{k}{k+1}.$$

Then, adding $1/(k+1)(k+2)$ to both sides of this equation, we obtain

$$\sum_{i=1}^{k+1} \frac{1}{i(i+1)} = \frac{k}{k+1} + \frac{1}{(k+1)(k+2)} = \frac{k^2 + 2k + 1}{(k+1)(k+2)} = \frac{k+1}{k+2}.$$

Thus, the assertion is true for $n = k + 1$ if it is true for $n = k$. Since it is also true for $n = 1$, it is true for every positive integer n by I_1.

3. The result is clearly true for $n = 1$. Suppose that it is also true for $n = k$; i.e., suppose that

$$2^{2k} - 1 = 3q$$

for some integer q. Then

$$
\begin{aligned}
2^{2(k+1)} - 1 &= 2^{2k+2} - 2^{2k} + 2^{2k} - 1 \\
&= 2^{2k}(2^2 - 1) + 3q \\
&= 3(2^{2k} + q).
\end{aligned}
$$

Thus, by I_1, the result is true for every positive integer n.

8. (c) In this problem, one should write out the sum for at least the first 8 values of n. It is then not too difficult to guess that

$$\sum_{i=1}^{n} (-1)^{i-1} f_i = 1 + (-1)^{n-1} f_{n-1}.$$

If we define $f_0 = 0$, as we may since we then have $f_0 + f_1 = f_2$, we see that our guess is correct for $n = 1$. Now assume that

$$\sum_{i=1}^{k} (-1)^{i-1} f_i = 1 + (-1)^{k-1} f_{k-1}.$$

Then

$$\sum_{i=1}^{k+1} (-1)^{i-1} f_i = 1 + (-1)^{k-1} f_{k-1} + (-1)^k f_{k+1}$$

$$= 1 + (-1)^k (f_{k+1} - f_{k-1}) = 1 + (-1)^k f_k$$

since $f_{k+1} - f_{k-1} = f_k$ for all $k \geq 1$. Thus, the result is true for all $n \geq 1$ by I_1.

10. By direct calculation, it is easily shown that Binet's formula holds for $n = 1$ and $n = 2$. Assume that it is also true for $n = 1, 2, \ldots, k$ where $k \geq 2$. Then

$$f_{k+1} = f_k + f_{k-1} = \frac{\alpha^k - \beta^k}{\sqrt{5}} + \frac{\alpha^{k-1} - \beta^{k-1}}{\sqrt{5}}$$

$$= \frac{\alpha^{k-1}(\alpha + 1) - \beta^{k-1}(\beta + 1)}{\sqrt{5}} = \frac{\alpha^{k+1} - \beta^{k+1}}{\sqrt{5}}$$

since $\alpha^2 = \alpha + 1$ and $\beta^2 = \beta + 1$. This shows that the result is true in any particular case if it is true in the *two* preceding cases. Thus, in order to make the induction go, it was necessary to prove the result true for both $n = 1$ and $n = 2$. It then follows that it is true for $n = 3$, hence also for $n = 4$, and so on.

13. We let m be any fixed nonnegative integer and use induction on n. For $n = 0$, we have that

$$f_0 f_m + f_1 f_{m+1} = 0 \cdot f_m + 1 \cdot f_{m+1} = f_{m+1} = f_{0+m+1}.$$

Also, for $n = 1$, we have

$$f_1 f_m + f_2 f_{m+1} = 1 \cdot f_m + 1 \cdot f_{m+1} = f_m + f_{m+1} = f_{m+2} = f_{1+m+1}.$$

Thus, the result is true for both $n = 0$ and $n = 1$. Now suppose that it is true for $n = 0, 1, \ldots, k$ where $k \geq 1$. In particular, then

$$f_{k-1+m+1} = f_{k-1}f_m + f_k f_{m+1}$$

and

$$f_{k+m+1} = f_k f_m + f_{k+1}f_{m+1}.$$

But then

$$f_{k+1+m+1} = f_{k-1+m+1} + f_{k+m+1} = f_{k-1}f_m + f_k f_{m+1} + f_k f_m + f_{k+1}f_{m+1}$$
$$= (f_{k-1} + f_k)f_m + (f_k + f_{k+1})f_{m+1} = f_{k+1}f_m + f_{k+2}f_{m+1}$$

and the result is also true for $n = k + 1$. Therefore, the result is true for every positive integer n by I_2.

14. If we set $m = n - 1$ in the formula of Problem 13, we obtain

$$f_{2n} = f_{n+(n-1)+1} = f_n f_{n-1} + f_{n+1}f_n = f_n(f_{n-1} + f_{n+1})$$

so that $f_n | f_{2n}$.

Section 1.5

2. Suppose that the Archimedean axiom is false; i.e., suppose that $an < b$ for every integer n. Then the set C of all integers of the form $b - an$ is a set of only positive integers. By the well-ordering principle, C must have a least element. Let $b - am$ be the least element of C. But then $b - a(m + 1)$ is in C since C contains all integers of this form and yet $b - a(m + 1) < b - am$. This contradicts the fact that $b - am$ is the least element of C. Therefore, the original assumption is false and the Archimedean axiom is true.

Section 1.7

1. Each number in the sequence is of the form $100k + 11 = 4(25k + 2) + 3$ with k a nonnegative integer. Thus, every integer in the sequence leaves a remainder of 3 when divided by 4 and so cannot be a square.

4. Let a and $a + 1$ be integers. By the division algorithm there exist integers q and r with $0 \leq r < 2$ such that $a = 2q + r$. If $r = 0$, then a is even. If $r = 1$, then $a + 1 = (2q + 1) + 1 = 2(q + 1)$ and $a + 1$ is even.

7. If n is not divisible by 2 or 3, then n must be of the form $6k + 1$ or $6k + 5$. Note that $6k + 5 = 6(k + 1) - 1$. Thus, n must be of the form $6k \pm 1$ for some integer k. Then

$$n^2 + 23 = (6k \pm 1)^2 + 23 = 36k^2 \pm 12k + 24 = 12k(3k \pm 1) + 24,$$

and it is clear that $n^2 + 23$ is divisible by 24 if $k(3k \pm 1)$ is divisible by 2. If k is even, this is surely true. If k is odd, then $3k$ is odd and $3k \pm 1$ is even. Thus, the result is true in any case.

9. By the division algorithm, there exist integers u and r with $0 \leq r < |b|$, such that

$$a = |b|u + r.$$

Since $b < 0$, $|b| = -b$. Therefore, setting $-u = q$, we obtain

$$a = -bu + r = bq + r$$

as desired.

Section 1.8

1. $247_{10} = 502_7 = 187_{12}$ **2.** $324_6 = 124_{10}$, $10_7 = 7_{10}$, $100_6 = 36_{10}$

3. $21.7_8 = 2 \cdot 8 + 1 + 7 \cdot 8^{-1} = 17.875_{10}$

4. (b) In octal notation one has the following:

$$
\begin{array}{r}
257 \\
361 \\
\hline
257 \\
2032 \\
1015 \\
\hline
122277
\end{array}
$$

5. (c) Using base 5 one has the following:

$$
\begin{array}{r}
12 \\
23\overline{\smash)331} \\
23 \\
\hline
101 \\
101 \\
\hline
\end{array}
$$

Section 2.1

3. Since $m|(35n + 26)$ and $m|(7n + 3)$, it follows from (v) of Theorem 2.1 that

$$m|[(35n + 26) - 5(7n + 3)].$$

Thus, $m|11$. Since $m > 1$ and 11 is a prime, it follows that $m = 11$.

6. Since $b|a$ and $r = a - bq$, it follows that $b|r$. Then, by Theorem 2.2, $|b| \leq r$ if $r \neq 0$. But we are given that $r < b$. Therefore, it must be the case that $r = 0$.

Section 2.3

1. $(357, 629) = 17 = 357 \cdot (-7) + 629 \cdot 4$.

4. Since $0 = 0 \cdot |b|$ and $b = \pm 1 \cdot |b|$, it is clear that $|b|$ is a common divisor of 0 and b. Suppose that f is any other common divisor. Then $f|b$ and $|f| \leq |b|$ by Theorem 2.2 since $b \neq 0$. But then $f \leq |b|$. Thus, no common divisor of 0 and b exceeds $|b|$ and $|b| = (0, b)$ by definition.

6. Let $d = (a, b)$ and $e = (a + c, b)$. Then $d|a$, $d|b$, $e|(a + c)$, $e|b$, $d > 0$, and $e > 0$. Since $b|c$, it also follows, by (iv) of Theorem 2.1, that $d|c$ and $e|c$. Now, since $d|a$ and $d|c$, $d|(a + c)$. Since we also have $d|b$, it follows from Theorem 2.5 that $d|e$. Conversely, since $e|c$ and $e|(a + c)$, $e|a$. Since we also have $e|b$, it again follows from Theorem 2.5 that $e|d$. But then, by Corollary 2.3, $e = d$, and the proof is complete.

7. Suppose that $(a, b) = d > 1$. Then $d|a$, $d|b$, and, since $b|c$, it follows that $d|c$. But then, by Theorem 2.5, $d|(a, c)$. This, however, is impossible since $(a, c) = 1$ and $d > 1$. Therefore, $(a, b) = 1$, and the proof is complete.

12. Let $d_1 = (d, m)$ and $d_2 = d/d_1$. Then $d_1 d_2 = d$ and $d_1|m$. Thus, it only remains to show that $d_2|n$. Let $m = Md_1$. Then, by Corollary 2.7, $(d_2, M) = 1$. Since $d|mn$, by hypothesis, there exists an integer q such that $dq = mn$. Hence, $d_1 d_2 q = Md_1 n$, $d_2 q = Mn$, and $d_2|Mn$. But $(d_2, M) = 1$, and so $d_2|n$ by Theorem 2.8.

15. In the first place, $(r, s) = 1$. For, if $(r, s) = d > 1$, then $d|r$, $d|s$, $d|b$, $d|c$, and this violates $(b, c) = 1$. Therefore, since $r|a$ and $s|a$, it follows from Theorem 2.13 that $rs|a$. Also, $r|b$ and $s|c$; so $rs|bc$. Therefore, if $e = (a, bc)$, we have that $rs|e$ by Theorem 2.5. Moreover, since $r = (a, b)$ and $s = (a, c)$, there exist integers x, y, u, v, such that

$$r = ax + by \quad \text{and} \quad s = au + cv.$$

Therefore

$$rs = a^2xu + acxv + abyu + bcyv,$$

and this implies that $e|rs$ since $e|a$ and $e|bc$. But then $rs = e = (a, bc)$ by Corollary 2.3.

18. Since $f_3 = 2$ and $f_3|f_{3q}$ for every $q \geq 1$ by Exercise 15, page 12, it follows that $2|f_n$ if $n = 3q$. To show the converse, we assume that $2|f_n$ and must show that $n = 3q$. Suppose that $n \neq 3q$ for any q. Then, by the division algorithm, there exist q and r with $0 < r < 3$ such that $n = 3q + r$. But then

$$f_n = f_{3q+r} = f_{3q-1}f_r + f_{3q}f_{r+1}$$

by the result of Exercise 13, page 12. Since $2|f_{3q}$ and $2|f_n$, it then follows that $2|f_{3q-1}f_r$. But $f_r = 1$ since $r = 1$ or 2, and $(2, f_{3q-1}) = 1$ since $2|f_{3q}$ and $(f_{3q}, f_{3q-1}) = 1$ by Exercise 16 above. Therefore $2 \nmid f_{3q-1}f_r$ and this is a contradiction. Therefore, $n = 3q$ as claimed.

Section 2.4

1. $[357, 629] = 13{,}209$.

2. $(357, 629, 221) = 17 = 357 \cdot (-7) + 629 \cdot 4 + 221 \cdot 0$.

3. $[357, 629, 221] = 171{,}717$.

6. In view of Theorem 2.16, the result will follow if we can show that

$$(9n + 8, 6n + 5) = 1.$$

Since

$$9n + 8 = (6n + 5) + (3n + 3)$$

and

$$6n + 5 = 2(3n + 3) - 1$$

it follows that if $d|(9n + 8)$ and $d|(6n + 5)$, then $d|(3n + 3)$ and $d|-1$. But then $d = \pm 1$. Thus, the largest common divisor of $9n + 8$ and $6n + 5$ is 1.

7. By the division algorithm there exist integers q and r with $0 \leq r < d$ such that $a_1 = dq + r$. Then

$$r = a_1 - dq = a_1 - (a_1x_1 + a_2x_2 + \cdots + a_rx_r) \cdot q$$
$$= a_1(1 - qx_1) + a_2(-qx_2) + \cdots + a_r(-qx_r).$$

Thus, since r is again a linear combination of $a_1, a_2, \ldots, a_r$ and $r < d$, this contradicts the fact that d is the least positive element of this form unless $r = 0$. Therefore, $r = 0$ and $d|a_1$. Similarly, we show that $d|a_i$ for $i = 2, \ldots, r$. Finally, if $f|a_i$ for all i, then $f|d$ and $|f| \leq d$ by Theorem 2.2. Therefore, d is the greatest of all common divisors as claimed.

Section 2.5

1. (a) $4725 = 3^3 \cdot 5^2 \cdot 7$. (c) $3234 = 2 \cdot 3 \cdot 7^2 \cdot 11$.

2. $(4725, 3234) = 3 \cdot 7 = 21$. **3.** $[4725, 3234] = 2 \cdot 3^3 \cdot 5^2 \cdot 7^2 \cdot 11 = 727{,}650$.

4. $\tau(4725) = (3 + 1)(2 + 1)(1 + 1) = 24$,

$$\sigma(4725) = \frac{3^4 - 1}{3 - 1} \cdot \frac{5^3 - 1}{5 - 1} \cdot \frac{7^2 - 1}{7 - 1} = 9{,}920.$$

6. $(1 + 3^2 + 3^4 + 3^6)(1 + 5^2 + 5^4)(1 + 7^2) = 26{,}691{,}000$.

8. If $a_i = 2b_i$ for each i, then

$$a = \prod_{i=1}^{r} p_i^{2b_i} = \left(\prod_{i=1}^{r} p_i^{b_i} \right)^2.$$

Thus, if a_i is even for each i, then a is a square. Conversely, suppose that $a = c^2$ for some integer c. If p is a prime, then $p|a$ if and only if $p|c$. Thus, $c = \prod_{i=1}^{r} p_i^{c_i}$ with $c_i > 0$ for each i. Then

$$a = c^2 = \prod_{i=1}^{r} p_i^{2c_i}$$

gives a canonical representation for a. Since this representation is unique, it follows that $a_i = 2c_i$ for each i. Thus a_i is even for each i as desired.

12. Let $a_i = \prod_{j=1}^{n} p_j^{\alpha_{ij}}$ with $\alpha_{ij} \geq 0$ be the canonical representation of a_i for each i. By the obvious extension of the result of Exercise 11,

$$d = (a_1, a_2, \ldots, a_r) = \prod_{j=1}^{n} p_j^{u_j}$$

and

$$m = [a_1, a_2, \ldots, a_r] = \prod_{j=1}^{n} p_j^{v_j},$$

where u_j is the smallest of $\alpha_{1j}, \alpha_{2j}, \ldots, \alpha_{rj}$ for each j and v_j is the largest of $\alpha_{1j}, \alpha_{2j}, \ldots, \alpha_{rj}$ for each j. From this it is clear that

$$dm = \prod_{j=1}^{n} p_j^{u_j + v_j} = \prod_{j=1}^{n} p_j^{\alpha_{1j} + \alpha_{2j} + \cdots + \alpha_{rj}} = \prod_{i=1}^{r} a_i$$

if and only if at most one of the α_{ij} differ from zero for each j.

Section 2.6

2. If either s or t is of the form $3q$, then clearly $3|x$. If neither s nor t is of the form $3q$, then since

$$(3q + 1)^2 = 3(3q^2 + 2q) + 1$$

and

$$(3q + 2)^2 = 3(3q^2 + 4q + 1) + 1,$$

it follows that there exist u and v such that $s^2 = 3u + 1$ and $t^2 = 3v + 1$. But then

$$y = t^2 - s^2 = (3v + 1) - (3u + 1) = 3(v - u)$$

and $3|y$. The argument for 5 is completely analogous to the argument for 3.

6. Notice that the perpendiculars to sides x and y are also r_z. Connect the center of the circle with the vertices of the triangle. Then compute the area of the given triangle in two different ways, obtaining

$$A = \frac{xy}{2} = \frac{zr_z}{2} + \frac{yr_z}{2} - \frac{xr_z}{2}.$$

Thus,

$$r_z = \frac{xy}{z + y - x}$$

$$= \frac{2k^2 st(t^2 - s^2)}{k(t^2 + s^2) + k(t^2 - s^2) - 2kst}$$

$$= ks(t + s)$$

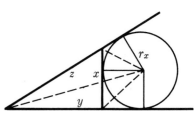

since $x = 2kst$, $y = k(t^2 - s^2)$, $z = k(t^2 + s^2)$ for suitable integers k, s, and t.

Section 3.2

3. Suppose that there are only finitely many primes of the form $4k + 1$, say p_1, $p_2, \ldots, p_r$, and consider the number

$$m = 4p_1p_2 \cdots p_r + 1,$$

which is of the form $4k + 1$. Since $m > p_i$ for $i = 1, 2, \ldots, r$ and $p_1, \ldots, p_r$ are the only primes of this form, m must be composite. Therefore, by the Fundamental Theorem of Arithmetic, m must have prime divisors. At this point the argument of the proof of Theorem 3.3 breaks down since we cannot argue as we did there that m must (in this case) have a prime divisor of the form $4k + 1$. The difficulty is that the product of two numbers of the form $4k + 3$ is a number of the form $4k + 1$. Thus, all the prime factors of m could be of the form $4k + 3$.

Section 3.3

2. We are assuming that

(1)
$$\lim_{n \to \infty} \frac{n \log n}{p_n} = 1.$$

From this it follows that

(2)
$$\lim_{n \to \infty} \frac{p_{n+1}}{p_n} = \lim_{n \to \infty} \left[\frac{p_{n+1}}{(n + 1) \log (n + 1)} \cdot \frac{n \log n}{p_n} \cdot \frac{(n + 1) \log (n + 1)}{n \log n} \right]$$
$$= 1.$$

Also, since the logarithmic function is continuous and

$$\lim_{n \to \infty} \frac{n \log n}{p_n} > 0,$$

the logarithm of the limit in (1) is equal to the limit of the logarithm. Thus, we obtain

$$\lim_{n \to \infty} (\log n + \log \log n - \log p_n) = 0$$

or

$$\lim_{n \to \infty} \log n \cdot \left(1 + \frac{\log \log n}{\log n} - \frac{\log p_n}{\log n} \right) = 0.$$

Since the second factor in this last limit must tend to zero and since

$$\lim_{n\to\infty} \frac{\log\log n}{\log n} = 0,$$

it follows that

$$\lim_{n\to\infty} \frac{\log p_n}{\log n} = 1.$$

Now, for $x \ge 2$, determine n by the inequality

(3) $$p_n \le x < p_{n+1}.$$

Then $x \to \infty$ as $n \to \infty$ and conversely. Also

(4) $$n = \pi(p_n) \le \pi(x) \le \pi(p_{n+1}) = n+1$$

and

(5) $$\log p_n \le \log x < \log p_{n+1}.$$

From (3) and (5) we obtain

(6) $$\frac{p_n}{\log p_{n+1}} < \frac{x}{\log x} < \frac{p_{n+1}}{\log p_n}.$$

Combining (6) with (4) we obtain

(7) $$\frac{n}{p_{n+1}/\log p_n} < \frac{\pi(x)}{x/\log x} < \frac{n+1}{p_n/\log p_{n+1}}.$$

Now

(8) $$\lim_{n\to\infty} \frac{n}{p_{n+1}/\log p_n} = \lim_{n\to\infty} \frac{n\log p_n}{p_{n+1}} = \lim_{n\to\infty}\left(\frac{n\log n}{p_n}\cdot\frac{p_n}{p_{n+1}}\cdot\frac{\log p_n}{\log n}\right) = 1$$

by (2), (3), and the hypothesis. Similarly

$$\lim_{n\to\infty} \frac{n+1}{p_n/\log p_{n+1}} = \lim_{n\to\infty} \frac{(n+1)\log p_{n+1}}{p_n}$$

(9)

$$= \lim_{n\to\infty}\left[\frac{(n+1)\log(n+1)}{p_{n+1}}\cdot\frac{p_{n+1}}{p_n}\cdot\frac{\log p_{n+1}}{\log(n+1)}\right] = 1.$$

But, since $x \to \infty$ as $n \to \infty$, (7), (8), and (9) together imply that

$$\lim_{x\to\infty} \frac{\pi(x)}{x/\log x} = 1$$

as desired.

Section 3.4

1. $F(n+k) - 2 = 2^{2^{n+k}} - 1 = (2^{2^n})^{2^k} - 1$.   Let $f(x) = x^{2^k} - 1$.   Then $f(-1) = 0$ and so, by the factor theorem from algebra, $f(x)$ has $x+1$ as a factor. Therefore, taking $x = 2^{2^n}$, we have that $2^{2^n} + 1$ is a factor of $(2^{2^n})^{2^k} - 1$ and thus that $F(n)|[F(n+k) - 2]$ since $F(n) = 2^{2^n} + 1$ and $f(2^{2^n}) = F(n+k) - 2$. Therefore, if $d = (F(n), F(n+k))$, it follows that $d|2$ and $d = 1$ or 2. But $F(n)$ is odd for every n and so $d = 1$ as claimed.

Section 4.2

2. (b) The relations of "less than" or "greater than" for real numbers.

3. 0

4. Since $3^2 \equiv 4 \equiv -1 \pmod 5$,

$$3^{20} \equiv (-1)^{10} = 1 \pmod 5.$$

Therefore, the least residues of 3^2 and 3^{20} modulo 5 are 4 and 1, respectively.

5. $10^{515} \equiv 5 \pmod 7$.

8. For any integer k, the numbers $k + 1, k + 2, \ldots, k + m$ are m consecutive integers. Since we have the correct number of numbers, it is only necessary to show that no two are congruent modulo m. Suppose that this is not so. Then there exist r and s with $1 \leq r < s \leq m$ such that

$$k + s \equiv k + r \pmod m.$$

This implies that $(s - r) \equiv 0 \pmod m$ so that $m | (s - r)$. But this is impossible since $0 < s - r \leq m - 1$. Thus, the assumption that two of the numbers in the above list were congruent modulo m must be false and the proof is complete.

14. If $17 | (5n^2 + 15)$, then $5n^2 + 15 \equiv 0 \pmod{17}$ and $n^2 \equiv -3 \pmod{17}$. On the other hand, since any 17 consecutive integers form a complete residue system modulo 17 by Exercise 8 above, any integer n is congruent modulo 17 to one of

$$0, \pm 1, \pm 2, \pm 3, \pm 4, \pm 5, \pm 6, \pm 7, \pm 8.$$

But then, by direct computation, n^2 is congruent modulo 17 to

$$0, 1, 4, 9, -1, 8, 2, -2, -4.$$

Thus, no n exists such that $n^2 \equiv -3 \pmod{17}$, and hence no n exists such that $17 | (5n^2 + 15)$.

16. Any integer n is congruent modulo 6 to one of $0, \pm 1, \pm 2, 3$. If n is not divisible by 2 or 3, then $n = \pm 1 \pmod 6$, and there exists an integer q such that $n = 6q \pm 1$. Therefore,

$$n^2 = 36q^2 \pm 12q + 1 = 12q(3q \pm 1) + 1 = 1 \pmod{24}$$

since either q or $3q \pm 1$ must be even.

20. If $a \equiv b \pmod m$ and $f(x)$ is a polynomial with integral coefficients, then $f(a) \equiv f(b) \pmod m$.

24. Modulo 3 any integer a is congruent to one of $-1, 0$, or 1. Consequently, a^3 is congruent to $-1, 0$, or 1, respectively, and $a^3 \equiv a \pmod 3$ in every case. Similarly, any a is congruent modulo 5 to one of $-2, -1, 0, 1$, or 2. Since $2^5 = 32 \equiv 2 \pmod 5$, it follows that $(-2)^5 \equiv -2 \pmod 5$. The computations are trivial in the other cases, and so again $a^5 \equiv a \pmod 5$ in every case.

25. Since $a^3 \equiv a \pmod 3$, it follows that $a^5 \equiv a^3 \equiv a \pmod 3$. Also $a^5 \equiv a \pmod 5$. Therefore, $3 | (a^5 - a)$ and $5 | (a^5 - a)$. Therefore, $15 | (a^5 - a)$ by Theorem 2.13, and $a^5 \equiv a \pmod{15}$ for every a. Alternatively, one can use the result of Exercise 22 above.

Section 4.3

2. Modulo 7 we note that $1 \equiv 1$, $10 \equiv 3$, $10^2 \equiv 2$, $10^3 \equiv -1$, $10^4 \equiv -3$, $10^5 \equiv -2$, $10^6 \equiv 1$, and that the consecutive subsequent powers of 10 will continue to repeat this pattern of residues. Now suppose that

$$n = a_n 10^n + a_{n-1} 10^{n-1} + \cdots + a_1 \cdot 10 + a_0$$

is the decimal representation of n. It then follows that

$$n \equiv a_0 + 3a_1 + 2a_2 - a_3 - 3a_4 - 2a_5 + a_6 + 3a_7 + \cdots \pmod 7$$

so that n is divisible by 7 if and only if

$$u = a_0 + 3a_1 + 2a_2 - a_3 - 3a_4 - 2a_5 + a_6 + 3a_7 + \cdots$$

is divisible by 7. The ambiguous dots are intended to indicate that the pattern $1, 3, 2, -1, -3, -2$ is repeated consecutively till all of the digits in the representation of n are used in the computation of u. For example, 20,135,738 is divisible by 7 since

$$8 + 3 \cdot 3 + 2 \cdot 7 - 1 \cdot 5 - 3 \cdot 3 - 2 \cdot 1 + 1 \cdot 0 + 3 \cdot 2 = 21$$

is divisible by 7.

5. Let a be the amount, in pennies, for which the check was originally written and let s be the sum of the digits in the decimal representation of a. Let b be the number which results from a transposition of the digits in a. Then, by the proof of Theorem 4.9, $a = s + 9u$ and $b = s + 9v$ for some integers u and v. Therefore, if e is the error,

$$e = a - b = 9(u - v)$$

and $9|e$ as claimed.

Section 4.4

3. By hypothesis, $a_i < a_{i+1}$ for each i, $(a_i, m) = 1$ for each i, $a_i \not\equiv a_j \pmod m$ if $i \ne j$, and $0 < a_i \le m - 1$ for each i. Consider the numbers $m - a_1$, $m - a_2, \ldots, m - a_{\phi(m)}$. Since $a_i < a_{i+1}$ for each i, it follows that $m - a_{i+1} < m - a_i$ for each i; i.e., $m - a_{\phi(m)} < m - a_{\phi(m)-1} < \cdots < m - a_1$. Since $m - a_i \equiv -a_i \pmod m$ for each i and since $a_i \not\equiv a_j \pmod m$ for $i \ne j$, it immediately follows that $m - a_i \not\equiv m - a_j \pmod m$ for $i \ne j$. Also, since $(-a_i, m) = (a_i, m) = 1$ and $m - a_i \equiv -a_i \pmod m$, it follows from Theorem 4.10, that $(m - a_i, m) = 1$ for each i. Finally, since $0 < a_i \le m - 1$ for each i, it follows that $1 \le m - a_i < m$, or equivalently, since the numbers involved are integers, that $0 < m - a_i \le m - 1$. Finally, since $a_1, a_2, \ldots, a_{\phi(m)}$ are the only numbers which satisfy the given conditions and since $m - a_{\phi(m)}$, $m - a_{\phi(m)-1}, \ldots, m - a_1$ satisfy the same conditions, the two sets of numbers are identical and $a_1 = m - a_{\phi(m)}$, $a_2 = m - a_{\phi(m)-1}, \ldots, a_{\phi(m)-1} = m - a_2$, $a_{\phi(m)} = m - a_1$ as desired.

5. Since $\phi(p) = p - 1$, a reduced residue system modulo p must contain $p - 1$ integers, each relatively prime to p and no two of which are congruent modulo p. Thus, we have only to show that $(a^i, p) = 1$ for $i = 1, 2, \ldots, p - 1$ and that $a^i \not\equiv a^j \pmod p$ for $i \ne j$. The first of these results follows directly from Theorem 2.12, since $(p, a) = 1$. Now suppose that $a^i \equiv a^j \pmod p$ with $1 \le j < i \le p - 1$. Since $(a^j, p) = 1$ for each j, we may divide both sides of this congruence by a^j to obtain $a^{i-j} \equiv 1 \pmod{p}$ and $1 \leq i - j \leq p - 2$. But this violates the condition that $p - 1$ is the smallest positive value of e such that $a^e \equiv 1 \pmod{p}$. Therefore, $a^i \not\equiv a^j \pmod{p}$ for $i \neq j$ and the proof is complete.

8. Let n be the number of positive integers not exceeding p^α which are not relatively prime to p^α. Then $\phi(p^\alpha) = p^\alpha - n$, and we have only to determine n. This is easily done since the integers not exceeding p^α which have a non-trivial factor in common with p^α are just the numbers $p, 2p, \ldots, p^{\alpha-1} \cdot p$; i.e., they are just the multiples of p which do not exceed p^α. Since there are $p^{\alpha-1}$ such numbers, $n = p^{\alpha-1}$ and

$$\phi(p^\alpha) = p^\alpha - p^{\alpha-1} = p^{\alpha-1}(p - 1).$$

9. This question can be answered by direct computation and counting. However, it is easier to evaluate $\phi(16 \cdot 9)$ by a method similar to that of the solution of the preceding problem. Let n be the number of values of m with $(m, 16 \cdot 9) > 1$ and $1 \leq m \leq 16 \cdot 9$. If $(m, 16 \cdot 9) > 1$, then clearly $2|m$ or $3|m$ or both. The multiples of 2 which do not exceed $16 \cdot 9$ are $2, 2 \cdot 2, 3 \cdot 2, \ldots, (8 \cdot 9) \cdot 2$, and there are $8 \cdot 9$ such numbers. Similarly, the $16 \cdot 3$ numbers $3, 2 \cdot 3, 3 \cdot 3, \ldots$, $(16 \cdot 3) \cdot 3$ are the multiples of 3 which do not exceed $16 \cdot 9$. Of course, multiples of 6 are multiples of both 2 and 3 and so appear in each of the above sequences. The multiples of 6 for which this is so are $6, 2 \cdot 6, \ldots, (8 \cdot 3) \cdot 6$, and there are $8 \cdot 3$ such numbers. Therefore, it follows that

$$m = 8 \cdot 9 + 16 \cdot 3 - 8 \cdot 3$$

and hence that

$$\phi(16 \cdot 9) = 16 \cdot 9 - 8 \cdot 9 - 16 \cdot 3 + 8 \cdot 3$$
$$= 8 \cdot 9 - 8 \cdot 3 = 8 \cdot 6 = \phi(16)\phi(9).$$

11. By Fermat's theorem, $p^{q-1} \equiv 1 \pmod{q}$. Since $q^{p-1} \equiv 0 \pmod{q}$, it therefore follows that

$$p^{q-1} + q^{p-1} \equiv 1 \pmod{q}.$$

Similarly, we obtain

$$p^{q-1} + q^{p-1} \equiv 1 \pmod{p}.$$

These imply that $q|(p^{q-1} + q^{p-1} - 1)$ and $p|(p^{q-1} + q^{p-1} - 1)$ and hence, by Theorem 2.13, that $pq|(p^{q-1} + q^{p-1} - 1)$. But this implies that

$$p^{q-1} + q^{p-1} \equiv 1 \pmod{pq}.$$

14. Since $\binom{p}{k} = p!/k!(p - k)!$ is a binomial coefficient, it is an integer. Moreover, for $1 \leq k \leq p - 1$, each factor of $k!$ and $(p - k)!$ is relatively prime to p. Therefore, in simplifying $\binom{p}{k}$ for such values of k, the p in the numerator cannot be divided out. That is $\binom{p}{k} = p \cdot q_k$ for each such k and $\binom{p}{k} \equiv 0 \pmod{p}$.

17. By Fermat's theorem, we have

$$(a + b)^p \equiv a + b \pmod{p}, \qquad a^p \equiv a \pmod{p},$$

and

$$b^p \equiv b \pmod{p}.$$

Combining these results, we immediately have

$$(a + b)^p \equiv a^p + b^p \pmod{p}.$$

Section 5.2

1. (a) 5   (b) 2, 5, 8   (c) 45, 94   (d) No solution.

2. $x_k = 5 + 7k$, $y_k = 5 - 15k$ for $k = 0, \pm1, \pm2, \ldots$.

3. Let c, d, and t denote respectively the number of chicks, ducks, and turkeys purchased. Then c, d, and t are positive integers and the two conditions give

$$c + d + t = 100$$

and

$$\tfrac{1}{2}c + 3d + 10t = 100.$$

These combine to give $5d + 19t = 100$ which can be solved to yield $t = 5$, $d = 1$, $c = 94$.

7. As in the case of linear Diophantine equations with two unknowns, this can be solved by using the Euclidean algorithm to find u, v, and w such that

$$1 = (48, 17, -66) = 48u + 17v - 66w$$

and then multiplying through by 9 to obtain the solution

$$x = 9u,$$
$$y = 9v,$$
$$z = 9w.$$

Alternatively, and more generally, solving

$$48x + 17y - 66z = 9$$

is equivalent to solving

$$48x - 66z \equiv 9 \pmod{17}$$

which, in turn, is equivalent to solving

$$-3x + 2z \equiv 9 \pmod{17}.$$

Multiplying through by -6 and simplifying, we obtain

$$x \equiv 12z - 3 \pmod{17},$$

which is solvable for any z. Indeed, if $z = h$, we obtain $x_0 = 12h - 3$, $y_0 = 9 - 30h$ as a particular solution of

$$48x + 17y = 66h + 9$$

and $x_k = -3 + 12h + 17k$, $y_k = 9 - 30h - 48k$ as the general solution. Thus, the general solution of

$$48x + 17y - 66z = 9$$

is given by

$$\left.\begin{array}{l} x = -3 + 12h + 17k, \\ y = 9 - 30h - 48k, \\ z = h, \end{array}\right\} \text{where} \begin{cases} h = 0, \pm1, \pm2, \ldots, \\ k = 0, \pm1, \pm2, \ldots. \end{cases}$$

8. 20   **9.** 7, 22, 37, 52, 67, 82, 97

Section 5.3

1. The solution 23 is unique modulo 105.

2. A general solution is given by $2962 + 4620k$ for any integer k. Thus, the desired solution is -1658.

3. The solution 19 is unique modulo 60.

4. Solutions of $3x \equiv 7$ (mod 5), $x \equiv 1$ (mod 4), and $5x \equiv 2$ (mod 11) are, respectively, -1, 1, and -4. Using the Chinese remainder theorem to solve simultaneously the system

$$x \equiv -1 (\text{mod } 5),$$
$$x \equiv 1 \ (\text{mod } 4),$$
$$x \equiv -4 \ (\text{mod } 11),$$

we obtain 29 as a solution to this system and hence to the original one. The solution is unique modulo 220.

5. 188, 83

6. (a) 157   (b) 1543   (c) 6997   (d) 178, 463, 748, 1033, 1318, 1603

7. 59

9. By the Chinese remainder theorem, the system

$$x \equiv -1 \ (\text{mod } p_1),$$
$$x \equiv -2 (\text{mod } p_2),$$
$$\dots\dots\dots\dots\dots,$$
$$x \equiv -n \ (\text{mod } p_n),$$

is solvable. Let x_0 be a positive solution and set $a_i = x_0 + i$. Then $p_i | a_i$ for each i and $a_1, a_2, \dots, a_n$ are consecutive positive integers.

Section 5.4

1. (a) 89   (b) 18   (c) 1118

2. Since $2x^9 + 2x^6 - x^5 - 2x^2 - x = (x^5 - x)(2x^4 + 2x + 1)$, it follows that any integral value of x is a solution.

3. 51, 426, 801

6. Since $r(x)$ is linear, we may write $r(x) = ax + b$. Therefore,

$$f(x) \equiv (x - 2)(x - 3)q(x) + ax + b \ (\text{mod } 7)$$

and since $f(2) \equiv 5$ (mod 7) and $f(3) \equiv 2$ (mod 7), we obtain the system

$$2a + b \equiv 5 \ (\text{mod } 7),$$
$$3a + b \equiv 2 \ (\text{mod } 7).$$

Subtracting the first congruence from the second, we obtain $a \equiv -3$ (mod 7), and this implies that $b \equiv 4$ (mod 7). Therefore,

$$r(x) = -3x + 4$$

satisfies the given conditions.

Section 5.5

2. As indicated in the hint in the statement of the problem $p - 1 \equiv -1 \pmod{p}$, $p - 2 \equiv -2 \pmod{p}, \ldots, p - k \equiv -k \pmod{p}$. Therefore,

$$(p - 1)(p - 2) \cdots (p - k) \equiv (-1)^k k! \pmod{p}. \tag{1}$$

Also, since $h + k = p - 1$, it follows that $h = p - k - 1$ and $h! = (p - k - 1)!$ Combining this with (1), we now obtain

$$(p - 1)! \equiv (-1)^k h! k! \pmod{p}$$

or, on multiplying through by $(-1)^k$,

$$h! k! = (-1)^k (p - 1)! \equiv (-1)^{k+1} \pmod{p}$$

since $(p - 1)! \equiv -1 \pmod{p}$ by Wilson's theorem.

7. Certainly 1 and -1 are solutions of the given congruence. Moreover, if a is any solution, then $a^2 \equiv 1 \pmod{p^\alpha}$ and $p^\alpha | (a - 1)(a + 1)$. Since

$$(a + 1) - (a - 1) = 2$$

and p is odd, it is clear that p cannot simultaneously divide both $a + 1$ and $a - 1$. Therefore, $p^\alpha | (a + 1)$ or $p^\alpha | (a - 1)$. Thus, $a \equiv \pm 1 \pmod{p^\alpha}$, and it follows that 1 and -1 are the only solutions of the given congruence.

Section 5.7

1. 1, 3, 4, 5, 9   **2.** (a) -1 (b) 1   (c) -1 (d) -1 (e) 1   (f) -1

5. For $p \equiv 1 \pmod{12}$ or $p \equiv -5 \pmod{12}$.

9. $x^2 \equiv 295 \pmod{2717}$ is solvable if and only if the system

$$x^2 \equiv 295 \pmod{11},$$
$$x^2 \equiv 295 \pmod{13},$$
$$x^2 \equiv 295 \pmod{19},$$

is solvable, and the system is solvable if and only if each congruence is individually solvable. Since

$$\left(\tfrac{295}{19}\right) = \left(\tfrac{10}{19}\right) = \left(\tfrac{2}{19}\right)\left(\tfrac{5}{19}\right) = -1 \cdot \left(\tfrac{4}{5}\right) = -1,$$

the last congruence is not solvable. Thus, the system is not solvable.

14. (a) 1, 4   (b) 4, 15, 60, 71   (c) 137, 235, 302, 400

17. Suppose that there are only finitely many primes of the form $4k + 1$, say $p_1, p_2,$ $\ldots, p_r$, and consider the number

$$n = 4p_1^2 p_2^2 \cdots p_r^2 + 1.$$

Clearly $n > p_i$ for each i. Since n is of the form $4k + 1$ and exceeds all primes of this form, it must be composite. Therefore, by the Fundamental Theorem of Arithmetic, n must have prime divisors. By the result of Exercise 16, all prime divisors of n must be of the form $4k + 1$. Thus, $p_i | n$ for some i. But this implies that $p_i | 1$, and this is impossible.

20. (h) $\left(\tfrac{35}{179}\right) = -1$, $\left(\tfrac{55}{167}\right) = -1$, $\left(\tfrac{51}{151}\right) = -1$.

Section 5.8

1. 1, 6.

3. Since $(7, 28) = 7$, there are $\frac{28}{7} = 4$ seventh power residues modulo 29. They are 1, 12, 17, and 28.

4. In the proof of Lemma 5.24 it was shown that u is a solution of $x^m \equiv n \pmod{p}$ if and only if $u = q^s$ where q is a primitive root modulo p, and $sm \equiv a \pmod{p-1}$ where $n \equiv q^a \pmod{p}$. In the present problem we may take $q = 2$, $m = 7$, $a = 7$ since $12 \equiv 2^7 \pmod{29}$, and s must be a solution of $7s \equiv 7 \pmod{28}$. The 7 solutions 1, 5, 9, 13, 17, 21, and 25 each yield a solution to the given congruence; i.e., the desired solutions are 2, $2^5 \equiv 3$, $2^9 \equiv 19$, $2^{13} \equiv 14$, $2^{17} \equiv 21$, $2^{21} \equiv 17$, and $2^{25} \equiv 11$.

5. Since $n^{(p-1)/d} \equiv 1 \pmod{p}$, the given congruence is solvable and $n \equiv q^{kd} \pmod{p}$ where q is a primitive root modulo p. As in the solution of the preceding problem, u is a solution of the given congruence if and only if $u = q^s$ where s is a solution of $sm \equiv kd \pmod{p-1}$. Since $d \equiv (m, p-1)$, this congruence is solvable and has d incongruent solutions modulo $(p-1)$. Let the solutions for s be

$$a, \quad a + \frac{p-1}{d}, \quad a + 2\frac{p-1}{d}, \quad \cdots, \quad a + (d-1)\frac{p-1}{d}.$$

Then the corresponding solutions to $x^m \equiv n \pmod{p}$ are

$$q^a, \quad a^{q+(p-1)/d}, \quad \cdots, \quad q^{a+(d-1)(p-1)/d}$$

and these are d in number.

9. Suppose that m belongs to e modulo rs. Then $m^e \equiv 1 \pmod{rs}$, and it follows that $m^e \equiv 1 \pmod{r}$ and $m^e \equiv 1 \pmod{s}$. Therefore, by Theorem 5.17, $h|e$, $k|e$, and there exist integers u and v such that $hu = e$ and $kv = e$. Set $(h, k) = d$. Then $h = Hd$, $k = Kd$, and $(H, K) = 1$. From the above equations we now obtain $Hdu = Kdv$, which reduces to $Hu = Kv$. This implies that $H|Kv$ and since $(H, K) = 1$, that $H|v$. Thus, there exists q such that $Hq = v$. But then

$$e = kv = kHq = \frac{hk}{d}q = [h, k]q$$

and it follows that $[h, k]|e$.

Conversely, since $[h, k] = hK = Hk$,

$$m^{[h,k]} \equiv (m^h)^K \equiv 1 \pmod{r}$$

and

$$m^{[h,k]} \equiv (m^k)^H \equiv 1 \pmod{s}.$$

Since $(r, s) = 1$, this implies that

$$m^{[h,k]} \equiv 1 \pmod{rs}$$

and hence, again by Theorem 5.17, that $e|[h, k]$. Finally, since e and $[h, k]$ are both positive, it follows that $e = [h, k]$ as desired.

13. 2, 3, 8, 10, 11, 14, 15, 18, 19, 21, 26, 27

17. If q is a primitive root modulo p^2, then q belongs to $\phi(p^2) = p(p-1) > p-1$. Therefore, $q^{p-1} \not\equiv 1 \pmod{p^2}$. Conversely, suppose that $q^{p-1} \not\equiv 1 \pmod{p^2}$. Since q is a primitive root modulo p, $q^{p-1} \equiv 1 \pmod{p}$ and $(q, p) = 1$. Therefore, by the Euler-Fermat Theorem $q^{p(p-1)} \equiv 1 \pmod{p^2}$ since $\phi(p^2) = p(p-1)$. Suppose that q belongs to e modulo p^2. Then $e \mid p(p-1)$ and there exists $k > 0$ such that $ek = p(p-1)$. Since $q^e \equiv 1 \pmod{p^2}$, it follows that $q^e \equiv 1 \pmod{p}$ and hence that $(p-1) \mid e$. Therefore, there exists r such that $r(p-1) = e$. Combining this with $ek = p(p-1)$, we obtain $rk(p-1) = p(p-1)$. Thus, $rk = p$ and it follows that $k = 1$ or $k = p$. If $k = p$, then $e = p-1$, and this violates the condition that $q^{p-1} \not\equiv 1 \pmod{p^2}$. Therefore, $k = 1$, $e = p(p-1) = \phi(p^2)$, and q is a primitive root modulo p^2.

19. (c) Let $r = \operatorname{ind}_q m$ and $s = \operatorname{ind}_q n$. Then $m \equiv q^r \pmod{p}$ and $n \equiv q^s \pmod{p}$. Therefore, $m \equiv n \pmod{p}$ if and only if $q^r \equiv q^s \pmod{p}$, and this is so, by Corollary 5.19, if and only if $r \equiv s \pmod{p-1}$.

22. The given congruence is solvable if and only if there exists u such that $u^m \equiv n \pmod{p}$. By the results of Exercise 19, such a u exists if and only if $s = \operatorname{ind}_q u$ exists such that
$$ms \equiv \operatorname{ind}_q n \pmod{p-1}.$$

By Theorem 5.1, this is solvable for s if and only if $d \mid \operatorname{ind}_q n$ where $d = (m, p-1)$, i.e., if and only if there exists k such that $kd = \operatorname{ind}_q n$. But this is so if and only if $n \equiv q^{kd} \pmod{p}$ as claimed.

Section 6.1

2. Suppose that $(m, n) = 1$. Then
$$m = \prod_{i=1}^{r} p_i^{\alpha_i}$$
and
$$n = \prod_{i=r+1}^{r+s} p_i^{\alpha_i}$$
where $\alpha_i \geq 1$ for all i and where $p_1, p_2, \ldots, p_{r+s}$ are distinct primes. Then
$$mn = \prod_{i=1}^{r+s} p_i^{\alpha_i}.$$
Therefore,
$$q(mn) = a^{p(mn)} = a^{r+s} = a^r a^s = a^{p(m)} a^{p(n)} = q(m)q(n)$$
and q is multiplicative. On the other hand, $q(6) = a^2$, $q(4) = a$, and $q(6 \cdot 4) = a^2 \neq q(6)q(4)$. Thus, q is not completely multiplicative.

5. Since $\tau(n) = \prod_{i=1}^{r} (n_i + 1)$ if $n = \prod_{i=1}^{r} p_i^{n_i}$, it is clear that $\tau(n)$ is odd if and only if each n_i is even. And, by Exercise 8, page 36, this is so if and only if n is a square.

Section 6.2

1. (b) $\sum_{d|12} \left[\sum_{b|(12/d)} f(d)g(b) \right]$

$= \sum_{b|12} f(1)g(b) + \sum_{b|6} f(2)g(b) + \sum_{b|4} f(3)g(b) + \sum_{b|3} f(4)g(b)$
$\quad + \sum_{b|2} f(6)g(b) + \sum_{b|1} f(12)g(b)$

$= f(1)g(1) + f(1)g(2) + f(1)g(3) + f(1)g(4) + f(1)g(6) + f(1)g(12)$
$\quad + f(2)g(1) + f(2)g(2) + f(2)g(3) + f(2)g(6)$
$\quad + f(3)g(1) + f(3)g(2) + f(3)g(4)$
$\quad + f(4)g(1) + f(4)g(3)$
$\quad + f(6)g(1) + f(6)g(2)$
$\quad + f(12)g(1).$

Similarly, we obtain

$\sum_{b|12} \left[\sum_{d|(12/b)} f(d)g(b) \right]$

$= \sum_{d|12} f(d)g(1) + \sum_{d|6} f(d)g(2) + \sum_{d|4} f(d)g(3) + \sum_{d|3} f(d)g(4)$
$\quad + \sum_{d|2} f(d)g(6) + \sum_{d|1} f(d)g(12)$

$= f(1)g(1) + f(2)g(1) + f(3)g(1) + f(4)g(1) + f(6)g(1) + f(12)g(1)$
$\quad + f(1)g(2) + f(2)g(2) + f(3)g(2) \qquad\qquad + f(6)g(2)$
$\quad + f(1)g(3) + f(2)g(3) \qquad\qquad + f(4)g(3)$
$\quad + f(1)g(4) \qquad\qquad + f(3)g(4)$
$\quad + f(1)g(6) + f(2)g(6)$
$\quad + f(1)g(12).$

We note that precisely the same terms appear in each sum. In fact, the terms in the first row of the first array are just those in the first column of the second array, and so on.

Section 6.3

5. As shown in Exercise 2, page 100, $q(n)$ is multiplicative. Therefore, by Corollary 6.5, $F(n)$ is multiplicative. Thus, by Theorem 6.2, $F(n) = \prod_{i=1}^{r} F(p_i^{n_i})$ if $n = \prod_{i=1}^{r} p_i^{n_i}$. But

$$F(p_i^{n_i}) = \sum_{d|p_i^{n_i}} q(d) = q(1) + q(p_i) + \cdots + q(p_i^{n_i}) = 1 + an_i.$$

Therefore, $F(n) = \prod_{i=1}^{r} (1 + an_i)$.

6. $\tau_2(n) = \prod_{i=1}^{r} \binom{n_i + 2}{2}$ **7.** $\tau_3(n) = \prod_{i=1}^{r} \binom{n_i + 3}{3}$ **8.** $\tau_k(n) = \prod_{i=1}^{r} \binom{n_i + k}{k}$

Section 6.4

1. By direct calculation it is easy to show that $523{,}776 = 2^9(2^{10} - 1)$. Since 10 is not a prime this number is not perfect.

Section 6.6

1. Let $a_1, a_2, \ldots, a_{\phi(n)}$ be the positive integers a satisfying $(a, n) = 1, 0 < a < n$. Since $(n - a, n) = (a, n) = 1$ and $0 < n - a < n$ if $0 < a < n$, these same numbers can be written in the form $n - a_1, n - a_2, \ldots, n - a_{\phi(n)}$. Therefore, if S is the desired sum, we may write

$$S = a_1 + a_2 + a_3 + \cdots + a_{\phi(n)}$$

and

$$S = (n - a_1) + (n - a_2) + (n - a_3) + \cdots + (n - a_{\phi(n)}).$$

Adding the expressions we obtain

$$2S = n + n + \cdots + n = n \cdot \phi(n)$$

so that $S = \phi(n)n/2$ as desired.

5. Since f and μ are multiplicative, F is also multiplicative by Theorem 6.4. Therefore, $F(n) = \prod_{i=1}^{r} F(p_i^{\alpha_i})$ if $n = \prod_{i=1}^{r} p_i^{\alpha_i}$. Thus,

$$F(p_i^{\alpha_i}) = \sum_{d \mid p_i^{\alpha_i}} \mu(d)f(d) = 1 - f(p_i)$$

and $F(n) = \prod_{i=1}^{r} [1 - f(p_i)]$ as claimed.

6. Since $\mu(n)$ and $\phi(n)$ are multiplicative, it follows from Theorems 6.3 and 6.4 that $\alpha(n)$ is also multiplicative. Therefore, $\alpha(n) = \prod_{i=1}^{r} \alpha(p_i^{\alpha_i})$ by Theorem 6.2. Now

$$\alpha(p_i^{\alpha_i}) = \sum_{d \mid p_i^{\alpha_i}} \frac{\mu^2(d)}{\phi(d)}$$

$$= \frac{\mu^2(1)}{\phi(1)} + \frac{\mu^2(p_i)}{\phi(p_i)} + \frac{\mu^2(p_i^2)}{\phi(p_i^2)} + \cdots$$

$$= 1 + \frac{1}{p_i - 1} + 0$$

$$= \frac{p_i}{p_i - 1}$$

$$= \frac{p_i^{\alpha_i}}{p_i^{\alpha_i - 1}(p_i - 1)}.$$

Therefore,

$$\alpha(n) = \prod_{i=1}^{r} \frac{p_i^{\alpha_i}}{p_i^{\alpha_i - 1}(p_i - 1)} = \frac{n}{\phi(n)}.$$

8. By the Möbius inversion formula

$$g(n) = \sum_{d \mid n} \mu(d) \cdot \frac{n^2}{d^2} = n^2 \sum_{d \mid n} \frac{\mu(d)}{d^2}.$$

Also, since $F(n) = n^2$ is multiplicative, $g(n)$ is multiplicative by Theorem 6.10.

Therefore,

$$g(n) = \prod_{i=1}^{r} g(p_i^{\alpha_i})$$

for $n = \prod_{i=1}^{r} p_i^{\alpha_i}$. Now

$$g(p_i^{\alpha_i}) = p_i^{2\alpha_i} \sum_{d \mid p_i^{\alpha_i}} \frac{\mu(d)}{d^2} = p_i^{2\alpha_i}\left(1 - \frac{1}{p_i^2}\right) = p_i^{2\alpha_i-2}(p_i^2 - 1)$$

so that

$$g(n) = \prod_{i=1}^{r} p_i^{2\alpha_i-2}(p_i^2 - 1).$$

This can be simplified further to

$$g(n) = \phi(n) \prod_{i=1}^{r} p_i^{\alpha_i-1}(p_i + 1).$$

10. The principal difficulty in this problem is notational. For $a = \prod_{i=1}^{t} p_i^{a_i}$ with $a_i \geq 1$ for all i, we may write

$$\phi(a) = \prod_{i=1}^{t} p_i^{a_i-1}(p_i - 1) = \prod_{i=1}^{t} p_i^{a_i}\left(1 - \frac{1}{p_i}\right) = a \prod_{i=1}^{t}\left(1 - \frac{1}{p_i}\right).$$

Moreover, if we define $\delta(0) = 0$ and $\delta(n) = 1$ if $n \neq 0$, we may write

$$\phi(a) = a \prod_{i=1}^{t}\left(1 - \frac{1}{p_i}\right)^{\delta(a_i)}$$

where $a = \prod_{i=1}^{t} p_i^{a_i}$ with $a_i \geq 0$ for all i. This device is to allow for the use of zero exponents in the canonical representation of a. Now let

$$m = \prod_{i=1}^{r} p_i^{m_i}, \qquad n = \prod_{i=1}^{r} p_i^{n_i}, \qquad d = \prod_{i=1}^{r} p_i^{d_i},$$

with $m_i \geq 0$, $n_i \geq 0$, $n_i + m_i \neq 0$, and d_i equal to the smaller of m_i and n_i for each i. Then, using δ as defined above, we have that

$$\frac{d\phi(m)\phi(n)}{\phi(d)} = \frac{dmn \prod_{i=1}^{r}\left(1 - \frac{1}{p_i}\right)^{\delta(m_i)} \prod_{i=1}^{r}\left(1 - \frac{1}{p_i}\right)^{\delta(n_i)}}{d \prod_{i=1}^{r}\left(1 - \frac{1}{p_i}\right)^{\delta(d_i)}}$$

$$= mn \prod_{i=1}^{r}\left(1 - \frac{1}{p_i}\right)^{\delta(m_i)+\delta(n_i)-\delta(d_i)} = \phi(mn)$$

since $\delta(m_i) + \delta(n_i) - \delta(d_i) = 1$ for each i and $mn = \prod_{i=1}^{r} p_i^{m_i+n_i}$ with $m_i + n_i \geq 1$ for each i. To see that $\delta(m_i) + \delta(n_i) - \delta(d_i) = 1$ for each i, we note that if $m_i > 0$ and $n_i > 0$, then $d_i > 0$ and

$$\delta(m_i) + \delta(n_i) - \delta(d_i) = 1 + 1 - 1 = 1.$$

On the other hand, if one of m_i or n_i is zero, the other is not zero and d_i is zero. Thus, $\delta(d_i) = 0$, one of $\delta(m_i)$ and $\delta(n_i)$ is zero and the other is 1.

Section 6.7

1. Let $f(n) = n^2$ and $s(n) = \sum_{k=1}^{n} f(k)$. Then

$$s\left(\frac{n}{d}\right) = \sum_{k=1}^{n/d} k^2 = \frac{n}{6d}\left(\frac{n}{d} + 1\right)\left(\frac{2n}{d} + 1\right)$$

and, by Theorem 6.17,

$$\sum_{\substack{k=1 \\ (k,n)=1}}^{n} k^2 = \sum_{d|n} \mu(d)d^2 \cdot \frac{n}{6d}\left(\frac{n}{d} + 1\right)\left(\frac{2n}{d} + 1\right)$$

$$= \frac{n}{6} \sum_{d|n} \mu(d)d\left(\frac{2n^2}{d^2} + \frac{3n}{d} + 1\right)$$

$$= \frac{n}{6}\left[2n^2 \sum_{d|n} \frac{\mu(d)}{d} + 3n \sum_{d|n} \mu(d) + \sum_{d|n} d\mu(d)\right]$$

$$= \frac{n}{6}\left[2n\phi(n) + \prod_{i=1}^{r} (1 - p_i)\right]$$

since

$$n \sum_{d|n} \frac{\mu(d)}{d} = \phi(n)$$

by Theorem 6.13,

$$\sum_{d|n} \mu(d) = 0$$

by Theorem 6.9 since $n > 1$, and

$$\sum_{d|n} d\mu(d) = \prod_{i=1}^{r} (1 - p_i)$$

by the result of Exercise 5, page 112.

Section 6.8

1. (b) -4 (f) -3 (k) -1 (l) 19

2. (a) If $\alpha = n + \theta$ with $0 \leq \theta < \frac{1}{2}$, then $[\alpha] = n$ and $[2\alpha] = 2n$ by part (f) of Theorem 6.21. If $\frac{1}{2} \leq \theta < 1$, then $[\alpha] = n$, $[2\alpha] = 2n + 1$, and $[2\alpha] = 2[\alpha] + 1$.

4. It suffices to show that $|[\alpha + \frac{1}{2}] - \alpha| \leq \frac{1}{2}$. By part (a) of Theorem 6.21, we have that

$$\alpha - \frac{1}{2} < [\alpha + \frac{1}{2}] \leq \alpha + \frac{1}{2}.$$

Therefore,

$$\frac{1}{2} < [\alpha + \frac{1}{2}] - \alpha \leq \frac{1}{2}$$

and so $|[\alpha + \frac{1}{2}] - \alpha| \leq \frac{1}{2}$. Suppose that two integers are equally near α. Then $\alpha = n + \frac{1}{2}$ for some integer n, $\alpha + \frac{1}{2} = n + 1$, and $[\alpha + \frac{1}{2}] = n + 1$. Thus, in this case, $[\alpha + \frac{1}{2}]$ is the larger of the two integers equally near α.

12. By definition $[\alpha] \leq \alpha$ and $[\beta] \leq \beta$. Therefore, $[\alpha] + [\beta] \leq \alpha + \beta$. But then, by part (b) of Theorem 6.21, $[\alpha] + [\beta] \leq [\alpha + \beta]$.

Index